Mike Grant

GW00384853

Sta. Cruz de Tenerife

PROVINCIA DE
STA. CRUZ DE TENERIFE

LANZAROTE

OCEANO   ATLANTICO

LA PALMA   TENERIFE

FUERTEVENTURA

GOMERA

GRAN CANARIA

HIERRO

PROVINCIA DE LAS PALMAS

ESCALA GRÁFICA

0   10 km

Parque Nac.

Garajonay

S. Sebastián
de la Gomera

GOMERA

Cover design: *Alfredo Anievas*

FOURth EDITION

© EDITORIAL EVEREST, S. A.
Ctra. León-La Coruña, km 5 - LEÓN
ISBN: 84-241-4496-1
Legal deposit: LE. 94-1990
Printed in Spain

EDITORIAL EVERGRÁFICAS, S. A.
Ctra. León-La Coruña, km 5
LEÓN (Spain)

Juan Alberto Rodríguez Pérez

Botanist and Technical Fruit-horticulturist and Gardening Engineer.
Curator of the Garden of Plant Acclimatization of La Orotava.

THE EXOTIC FLORA OF THE CANARY ISLANDS

Translated by: Edward Barreto and Pilar P. de Valdelomar

Photographs by the author

BOOK OF NATIONAL TOURISTIC INTEREST

EDITORIAL EVEREST, S. A.

MADRID • LEON • BARCELONA • SEVILLA • GRANADA • VALENCIA
ZARAGOZA • LAS PALMAS DE GRAN CANARIA • LA CORUÑA
PALMA DE MALLORCA • ALICANTE – MEXICO • BUENOS AIRES

INTRODUCTION

The incorporation of the Canary Islands into the Spanish Crown brought about the introduction of quite a lot of species of plants. As the Canary Islands were an obligatory stop for all the European ships covering the routes to America, Asia an Africa, the great number of Canarian immigrants to Latin American countries, together with the establishing in Tenerife of the Garden of Plant Acclimatization La Orotava, contributed decisively in collecting the nearly countless variety of trees, shrubs and herbaceous species today existing in our archipelago. These species come from the most distant places in the planet.

Our public and private gardens are literally packed with beautiful exotic species. There are plants brought from Australia, such as the Grevillea *(Grevillea robusta)*, or the Fire Tree *(Brachychiton acerifolium)*; from Madagascar, for instance the Flamboyant *(Delonix regia)* or the Pandan *(Pandanus utilis)*; from South America, like the Jacaranda *(Jacaranda mimosifolia)* or the Ombú *(Phytolacca dioica)*; from India, such as the Orchid Tree *(Bauhinia variegata)*, and from tropical Africa, such as the Tulip Tree from Gabon *(Spathodea campanulata)* to mention a few.

All these plants and many more that would result cumbersome to mention here, are part of our daily life. They beautify our streets, avenues, parks and gardens, playing a key role in the reduction of air pollution as well as in regulating the

4

prevailing temperature and air humidity factors. They are, therefore, active members of our community. For these reasons we must try and know them better, so that we can understand the work they perform more in detail and at the same time learn to· love and respect them.

The purpose of this book is to make available to all the people from the Canary Islands as well as the tourists that visit us, a brief, practical guide for the 107 species of palm trees, trees and exotic shrubs that can be seen growing in the gardens, squares and parks of the islands.

The species have been arranged in alphabetical order by their scientific names. The description of every species includes its scientific name, family, habitat, common name, morphologic characteristics, growth conditions, services it offer to man, its use in gardening, flowering or fructification, and propagation manner. All the flowering and fructification data has been collected at Puerto de la Cruz, Tenerife.

The last pages of the book include a glossary of botanical terms to help readers not familiar with this vocabulary to have a better understanding of the book.

The author thanks Carlos González Martín, Botanist Master of the Garden of Plant Acclimatization La Orotava for his collaboration in the making of this book.

Acacia farnesiana. General view.

Acacia farnesiana (L.) Willd. Leguminosae. Tropical and Sub-tropical America. SWEET ACACIA.

Thorny, evergreen shrub that can reach a height of 6 meters. Bipinnate leaves up to 7.5 centimeters long. Oblong-linear folioles up to 5 mm long. Yellow flowers, very fragant, in globose capitula, up to 1.8 cm in diameter, grouped in small racemes. Fruit in pods, brown to blackish up to 7.5 cm long. Brownish seeds up to 7 mm long.

It grows well on most soils, though it thrives in sunny areas, and withstands droughts.

This shrub is cultivated for the obtention of a perfume from its flowers that is used in the perfume industry. The foliage is used in Australia as casttle fodder.

In gardening it is used solitary or in groups and for making hedges.

Flowering: Autumn-winter.

Propagation: Seeds.

Acacia farnesiana. Flowers.

Acokanthera oblongifolia. General view.

Acokanthera oblongifolia. Flowers.

Acokanthera oblongifolia (Hochst.) Codd. [*A. spectabilis* (Sond.) Hook f.] Apocynaceae. South Africa. WINTERSWEET.

Evergreen shrub often seen reaching heights of 6 m. Opposite, ovate to elliptical leaves, leathery and shiny, up to 12 cm long. White flowers up to 1.8 cm in diameter, clustered in corymbs with jasmine-like scent. Berry fruits, ellipsoidal, globose, purple-blackish, with one or two seeds.

It prefers good soils, moist and partly shaded.

All the parts of this plant are poisonous. Its sap is used in South Africa by some tribes of natives to poison their arrows. It also has medicinal properties.

It is used in gardening both in isolation or in groups.
Flowering: Autumn-spring.
Propagation: Seeds.

Albizia julibrissin. General view.

Albizia julibrissin. Flowers.

Albizia julibrissin Durazz. Leguminosae. Iran through Japan. SILK TREE.

Deciduous tree up to 12 m high. Bipinnate leaves up to 30 cm long and at times longer. Oblong-curved folioles, up to 18 mm long, with the midvein located near one of the edges. Pink flowers in capitula grouped at ends of twigs. Fruits in pods up to 15 cm long.

It prefers siliceous soils and is resistant to drought, and to temperature as low as −10° C.

It is seen in parks and gardens as well as aligning streets.

Flowering: Spring-summer.
Propagation: Seeds.

11

Aleurites moluccana. General view.

Aleurites moluccana. Fruit.

Aleurites moluccana (L.) Willd [*A. triloba* J. R. Forst. et G. Forst] Euphorbiaceae. Tropical Asia and Pacific Islands. CANDLENUT TREE.

Evergreen tree that grows up to 18 m high. Large, ovate, often angular or lobate leaves. Petioles up to 35 cm long. Blades up to 23 cm long. Small whitish flowers grouped in cymes. Globose fruits, up to 5 cm in diameter, with 1 or 2 large seeds with approximately 60 % oil.

This tree grows on most soils and conditions as long as there is abundant water. It grows fast. In Tenerife it is both seen on the coast and in the midlands, living perfectly in La Laguna. It is cultivated in tropical countries for the obtention of oil from its seeds used in varnishes and as fuel. It is also used as a shade tree.

Flowering: Autumn.

Propagation: Seeds and stem cutting.

13

Araucaria heterophylla. General view.

Araucaria heterophylla. Leaves.

Araucaria heterophylla (Salisbl.) Franco. Araucariaceae. Island of Norfolk. ARAUCARIA, NORFOLK PINE.

Evergreen tree that can be seen reaching 60 m. Verticillated, horizontal branches. The young needles are pointed and curved inwards. The adult needles are lance-shaped or ovate-triangular, imbricate. Globular, feminine cones, 12-15 cm in diameter and alate, elongated seeds.

It grows on most soils and resists the proximity of the ocean. It prefers sunny or semishaded areas. It grows fast.

This tree is cultivated as a decorative plant; its use as a garden species is restricted to large gardens and parks because the large roots constitute a danger to nearby buildings.

Propagation: Seeds, stem cutting and grafting.

15

Archontophoenix cunninghamiana. General view.

Archontophoenix cunninghamiana. Fruit.

Archontophoenix cunningha-mania (H. Wendl.) H. Wendl. et Drude. Palmae. Australia. PICCABEEN PALM.

Monoecious palm measuring up to 20 m high, with a sleek, ringed trunk. Pinnate leaves up to 3 m long. Branched inflorescences beneath the leaves with lilac flowers. Globular red fruits approximately 1.2 cm in diameter.

It grows on humid, rich soils, semishaded, although it can grow in open or shaded spaces. In Tenerife it can be seen growing in the heights of La Laguna.

This palm is used in gardening, as an aligning tree, for forming groups or as a solitary stand. It is also used in interior decoration.

Propagation: Seeds.

17

Arescastrum romanzoffianum var. australe. General view.

Arecastrum romanzoffianum var. australe. Fruit.

Syagrus romanzoffiana (Cham.) Glassman var. australe (Mart.) Becc [Arecastrum romanzoffianum (Cham.) Becc. var. australe (Mart.) Becc.] Palmae. Brazil to Argentina. QUEEN PALM

Monoecious palm that can reach 12-15 m high, with a grayish, ringed trunk. Pinnate leaves over 4.5 m long, arranged in different levels along the rachis. Branched inflorescences up to 90 cm that appear among the leaves, with small cream colored flowers. It has oval yellow fruits approximately 2.5 cm long, with the endocarp narrowing at the ends.

This palm grows on any conditions though it prefers sunny areas; it withstands the proximity of the ocean and grows fast. It substitutes the Royal Palm Tree in areas where the latter cannot be cultivated.

It is widely cultivated in tropical and subtropical gardens in groups or alone. It is also used in streets and avenues for aligning purposes.

Propagation: Seeds.

19

Artocarpus altitis.
General view.

Artocarpus altilis (Parkins.) Fosb. [*A. incisus* L. f.] Moraceae Malasia. BREAD-FRUIT TREE.

Evergreen tree, monoecious, reaching over 15 m high. Large, ovate, pinnate-lobate, leathery leaves up to 90 cm long, dark green above, paler beneath. Male flowers grouped in clustered spikes up to 30 cm long. Female flowers in subglobular capitulums. Round, muricated fruits, yellowish when ripe, up to 20 cm in diameter ·and made up of achenes grouped in a syncarp.

This tree prefers well drained, humid soils. It has a deep root system and needs to grow in hot areas.

This is a very ornamental species of trees, profusely used

in gardens in tropical countries. It is also cultivated for its fruit, which can substitute bread when baked. The fruits are rich in carbohydrates and in vitamins A, B and C. The seeds are edible when roasted, and the wood has been used to make canoes. The best quality trees of this species do not give seeds.

The breadfruit tree was introduced in tropical America to feed the black slaves. However, it did not prove successful, for other tropical plants such as the banana, yucca, etc., offered better fruits of easier and faster production.

Propagation: Seeds, stem cutting and root cutting.

Artocarpus altitis. Leaves.

*Artocarpus
heterophyllus.*
General view.

Artocarpus heterophyllus Lam. [A. *integrifolius* auct. non L. f.] Moraceae. India through the Malay Peninsula. JACKFRUIT.

Evergreen tree up to 15 m high. Entire, elliptical to obovate leaves up to 20 cm long, dark green above, paler beneath. Very small male flower grouped in cylindrical spikes or mace-shaped, up to 10 cm long. Female flowers in capitulums. Elongated fruits, up to 60 cm long, consisting of achenes grouped in a yellowish-greenish syncarp when ripe. The fruits grow on the older branches and on the trunk, sometimes weighing 15-20 kilograms.

This tree requires rich, deep, humid soils with plenty

of sun. It grows fast and is difficult to transplant.

The ripe fruits have an unpleasant smell, but the pulp, nevertheless, resembles the bananas in taste and it is eaten raw, cooked or fried, and it is used to make sauces. The green fruits are used as vegetables and the roasted seeds resemble chestnuts in taste. The wood is hardy and of good quality.

This tree is used in tropical gardens.

Propagation: Seeds and stem cutting.

Artocarpus heterophyllus. Inflorescence.

Bauhinia variegata. General view.

Bauhinia variegata L. Leguminosae. India. ORCHID TREE.

Briefly deciduous tree that can grow to be up to 6 m tall. Leaves up to 12 cm in diameter, compound, pinnate, formed by two joined folioles about 2/3 of its length from the base. Flowers up to 12 cm in diameter with overlapped petals, magenta-lavender, purple or white in color with the central petals dark purple. The flowers have 5 fertile stamens and are grouped in small lateral racemes at the ends of the twigs.

Cv. candida. The white

flowers have green veins. It does not require special soil or water conditions, and accepts shaded areas. It grows fast.

The bark, somewhat astringent, is used for dyes and tanning in India. The leaves and floral bottons are used as vegetables.

This tree is appropriate for small gardens to lend the touch of color, as well as for forming groups in large gardens. It is also used for alignment in narrow streets.

Flowering: Autumn through spring.

Propagation: Seeds and stem cutting.

Bauhinia variegata. Flowers.

Brachychiton acerifolium (A. Cunn.) F. J. Muell [*Sterculia acerifolia* A. Cunn.] Sterculiaceae. Australia. FLAME TREE.

Deciduous tree, up to 30 m tall. Large, 3-5-7 lobate leaves, sometimes entire. Petioles up to 70 cm long. Blades up to 27 cm long. Bell-shaped scarlet flowers, 2 cm in diameter and clustered in panicles. Fruit in follicles, blackish, up to 10 cm long, provided with long peduncles. The seeds are yellow.

This tree adapts well to most kinds of soils and situations as long as it has abundant water. It grows fast.

Flowering takes place when the leaves have fallen and it is very spectacular, for then the tree resembles a torch. This tree is used for alignment in streets and avenues and is seen in most gardens and parks. When young it can be used as an indoors plant.

Flowering: Spring-summer.

Propagation: Seeds.

Brachychiton acerifolium. Flowers.

Brachychiton discolor. General view.

Brachychiton discolor. Flowers and fruit.

Brachychiton discolor F. J. Muell [*Sterculia discolor* (F. J. Muell.) F. J. Muell ex Benth.] Sterculiaceae. Australia. SCRUB BOTTLE TREE.

Deciduous tree seen towering up to 30 m tall. 3-5-7 lobated, angular leaves with a whitish tomentum beneath. Petioles that can be 17 cm long. Blades 30 cm long and 25 cm wide. Flowers grouped in recemes, without petals and with a pink or light red calyx, tomentose, bell-shaped and reaching lengths of up to 5 cm. Fruits in follicles up to 15 cm long, with rust colored pubescence.

This tree grows on most soils, though it prefers sunny areas. It grows fast.

It is used in gardens and parks as well as for alingning purposes.

Flowering: Spring-summer.
Propagation: Seeds.

Brachychiton populneum. General view.

Brachychiton populneum. Flowers.

Brachychiton populneum (Schott at Endl.) R. Br. [*B. Diversifolius* Hort., not. R. Br.; *Sterculia diversifolia* G. Don.]. Sterculiaceae. Australia. KURRAJONG.

This evergreen tree can be seen reaching heights of up to 20 m high. Ovate or ovate-lance-shaped leaves, entire or lobate, with 3-5 lobes. Petioles up to 7 cm long. Blades up to 15 cm long. White, yellowish-greenish flowers up to 1 cm in diameter. Fruits in follicle, blackish and up to 7 cm long. Yellow seeds.

This tree thrives in most regions and withstands low temperatures. It can survive droughts. In Australia its foliage is usedas cattle fodder.

It is used for urban alignment in streets and avenues as well as a shade tree in gardens. When young it can be used as an indoor plant.

Flowering: Later winter-spring-summer-autumn.

Propagation: Seeds.

31

Caesalpinia gilliesi (Wallich ex Hook.) Benth. [*Poinciana gilliesi* Wallich ex Hook.]. Leguminosae. Argentina, uruguay. BIRD OF PARADISE.

Deciduous shrub or small tree that can grow to be up to 6 m tall, with pubescent, glandular twigs. Bipinnate leaves up to 20 cm long. Oblong folioles up to 8 m long. Flowers in racemes growing at ends of twigs. Yellow petals up to 3 cm long; red stamens up to 9 cm long. Fruit in pods up to 10 cm long.

Caesalpinia gilliesii. General view.

Caesalpinia gilliesii. Flowers.

It grows well on most soils though it prefers sunny, rather dry areas. It grows fast. This shrub is used in tropical and subtropical gardens, either solitary or in groups.

Flowering: Spring through autumn.

Propagation: Seeds.

Caesalpinia pulcherrima. General view.

Caesalpinia pulcherrima. Flowers.

Caesalpinia pulcherrima (L.) Swartz. [*Poinciana pulcherrima* L.]. Leguminosae. The West Indies. BARBADOS PRIDE.

Deciduous shrub or small tree up to 6 m tall, aculeate and glabrous. Bipinnate leaves, with 3-9 pairs of folioles, oblong or oblong-spatulate in shape, up to 1.5 cm long. Flowers grouped in terminal clusters. Red petals with yellow edges. Red stamens up to 6.5 cm long. The petals are occasionally yellow or pink. Fruit in oblong-linear pods, up to 12 cm long.

It can grow on most soils although it favors dry, sunny areas. It grows fast.

This tree is widely used in the tropics and subtropics for its beauty. It is used alone or in groups. It is also cultivated as free-growing hedges in dry areas.

Flowering: Summer through winter.

Propagation: Seeds.

Carica papaya. L. Caricaceae.
Tropical America. PAPAYA.
PAPAW.

Semiwoody tree with an
average height of 3-6 m. The
palmatilobate leaves can
reach 60 cm in diameter.
There are male, female and
hermaphrodite plants. Yellow
female flowers 3.5 cm long
growing alone or in small
racemes up to 7.5 cm long.
Male white-creamish or pink
flowers up to 2.5 cm long,
growing in pendulous panicles,
27-75 cm long. The herma-
phrodite flowers are divided
into three types: elongate,
pentandriate and interme-
diate. Male and hermaphrodite can also produce female

flowers. The fruits resemble cantaloupes, with yellow or orange-reddish pulp.

Papaws prefer loam, rich and well-drained soils, with plenty of sun. It dies in stagnant water and grows fast. It withstands droughts up to certain extent.

It is cultivated for its fruit which is eaten fresh from the tree; the fruit is also very digestive owing to the papain, an alkaloid widely used in pharmaceutics. Preserves, jams, juices and other delicacies are made with it. In the island there are several orchards, the best well-know being 'Solo' y 'Puna'. Gardens acquire a tropical touch with this tree.

Propagation: Seeds.

Carica papaya. Leaves.

Caryota urens. General view.

Caryota urens L. Palmae. India, Shri Lanka and the Malay Peninsula. WINE PALM.

Monoecious palm with unbranched trunk that can reach 18 m high. Bipinnate leaves up to 6 m long. Folioles resembling fish tails up to 15 cm long. Branched inflorescences with pendulous sprigs and unisexual flowers. The inflorescences appear first on the higher part of the and gradually move down until the fruit in the lower part of the tree are ripe; this is when the tree dies. Globoid fruits, red purple when ripe, up to 1.5 cm in diameter. Its habitat is good, humid soils, although it can grow on harsh condi-

38

tions. It grows best in sunny areas and accepts shaded regions; it is a fast-growing tree.

In India and Shri Lanka the petioles of the leaves are used to obtain a fiber to make brooms and brushes. The sap is used to make palm tree wine and sugar of good quality. The medulla produces a sort of flour or «sago» (starch).

This palm tree is widely cultivated in tropical and subtropical gardens around the world. It is recommended for growing in patios.

Propagation: Seeds.

Caryota urens. Inflorescence.

Casimiroa edulis.
General view.

Casimiroa edulis Llave. Ruta-
ceae. Mexico. WHITE SA-
POTE.

Evergreen tree up to 15 m
tall or more. Palmaticom-
pound leaves with 3-5 folioles,
glabrous, ovate to oblong-
lanceshaped up to 17 cm long,
slightly festooned and ondu-
late. Petioles up to 12 cm long.

Small, white-greenish flowers
grouped in axillar racemes.
Yellow-greenish, edible, globose fruits up to 8 cm in diameter.

It grows well on thoroughly
drained, sandy loam soils.
The sun is good for this tree,
and accepts well cold conditions; it can grow in the

vicinity of orange groves. It grows fast.

This tree is cultivated in Mexico, Central America, Florida and California for its fruit with peach-like taste when eaten alone or with cream and sugar. In Mexico it is used to cure insonmia, for it is believed to have somniferous qualities. The leaves are used to cure diarrhea.

Fructification: Summer.

Propagation: Seeds and grafting.

Casimiroa edulis. Fruit.

Cassia didymobotrya. General view.

Cassia didymobotrya. Flowers.

Cassia didymobotrya Fresen. Leguminosae. Tropical Africa.

Evergreen shrub reaching up to 3 m tall. Pinnate leaves, up to 40 cm long. Oblong to ovate-elliptical folioles, with rounded apex, mucronate, up to 5 cm long. Flowers in upright racemes up to 30 cm long. Yellow petals and brown sepals. Fruit in pods up to 10 cm long.

It grows well on most kinds of soil, though it prefers dry, sunny areas. It grows fast.

This shrub is used in tropical and subtropical gardens owing to its beautiful flowers.

Flowering: Throughout the year.

Propagation: Seeds.

Cassia spectabilis. General view.

Cassia spectabilis. Flowers.

Cassia spectabilis DC. Leguminosae. Tropical America.

Deciduous tree sometimes reaching heights of 18 m, although in the Canary Islands it does not grow taller than 8 m. Paripinnate leaves up to 45 cm long. Ovate-lance-shaped folioles, tomentous, up to 8 cm long. Yellow flowers in terminal, upright panicles up to 60 cm long. Fruit in pods, cylindrical, up to 30 cm long, blackish in color.

This tree does not require special soils, though it needs the sun for flowering. It grows fast.

It is used in tropical and subtropical gardens for its splendid, beautiful flowers. It is also used for alignment in streets, avenues and roads.

Flowering: Summer-autumn.

Propagation: Seeds and stem-cutting.

45

Castanospermum australe. General view.

Castanospermum australe. Flowers.

Castanospermun australe A. Cunn. et C. Frasser. Leguminosae. Australia. MORETON BAY CHESNUT.

Evergreen tree up to 18 m tall. Imparipinnate, dark green, glossy leaves, up to 45 cm long. Oblong folicles up to 13 cm long. Yellow, orange to reddish flowers up to 4 cm long, grouped in lateral racemes up to 15 cm long. Fruit in pods up to 25 cm long.

It grows well on most soils and conditions, but requires sunny areas.

The seeds, resembling chestnuts, are edible and are eaten roasted.

It is utilized in parks for the beauty of its foliage, flowers and fruits. It is also used an indoor plant in flower-pots.

Flowering: Spring-summer.

Propagation: Seeds.

47

Cestrum aurantiacum. General view.

Cestrum aurantiacum. Flowers.

Cestrum aurantiacum Lindl.
Solanaceae. Guatemala.

Evergreen, semiclimbing shrub or small tree growing to be up to 6 m tall. Entire, ovate-lance-shaped leaves up to 15 cm long. Sessile, yellow flowers up to 2.5 cm long grouped in axillar and terminal racemes which are in turn grouped in terminal panicles. Fruit in berries, white, up to 1.2 cm in diameter.

This species grows on most soils and requires sunny or slightly shaded areas.

It is cultivated in gardens to cover walls exposed to the sun, both solitary or forming groups.

Flowering: Summer-autumn.
Propagation: Seeds and stem cutting.

49

Cestrum diurnum. General view.

Cestrum diurnum. Flowers.

Cestrum diurnum L. [*C. album* Ferrero ex Dunal]. Solanaceae. West Indies. DAY JESSAMINE.

Evergreen shrub that can grow to be 4.5 m tall. Oblong or oblong-elliptical leaves up to 10 cm long, obtuse or acute in the apex, glabrous. White flowers, quite flagrant in the daytime, grouped in elongated pedunculate racemes. Fruit in berries, almost globular, black in color.

It grows on most soils with plenty of sun or under some light shade. The shrub must be pruned when the fruits have been fallen.

It is used in gardening, solitary or in groups.

Flowering: Spring-summer-autumn.

Propagation: Seeds and stem-cutting.

Cestrum elegans. General view.

Cestrum elegans. Flowers.

Cestrum elegans (Brongn.) Schlechtend. [*C. purpureum* (Lindley) Standley]. Solanaceae. Mexico.

Evergreen, semiclimbing shrub, with pubescent, flexible branches, often seen reaching 4 m tall. Ovate-lance-shaped leaves, up to 19 cm long. Scarlet to purple reddish flowers up to 2 cm long grouped in pendulate panicles. Berry-like fruit, globular, purple in color.

It grows well on most soils and can be cultivated either in sunny or shaded areas. It generally sheds the leaves from the base of the branches.

It is widely cultivated in gardens for its abundant flowers. It is used alone or in groups. It also grows well in flowerpots.

Flowering: Almost throughout the year.

Propagation: Seeds and stem-cutting.

Cestrum nocturnum. General view.

Cestrum nocturnum. Flowers.

Cestrum nocturnum L. Solanaceae. West Indies. NIGHT JESSAMINE.

Evergreen shrub that can reach 3.5 m tall. Ovate-lance-shaped, narrow leaves, acuminate, up to 22 cm long. Beige, or white-greenish flowers, very fragrant at night, up to 2.5 cm long, clustered in axillar facemes. Berry-like fruit, white in color.

It tolerates most soils, though it requires sunny or slightly shaded areas. It is affected by droughts and requires an adequate treatment of fertilizers. It needs to be pruned regularly, for it tends to shed the lower leaves.

It is used in gardening alone or in groups to make hedges of informal type.

Flowering: Spring-summer-autumn.

Propagation: Seeds and cuttings.

Cestrum parqui. General view.

Cestrum parqui. Flowers.

Cestrum parqui L'Hér. Solanaceae. Chile. WILLOW-LEAVED JESSAMINE.

Evergreen shrub approximately up to 3.5 m tall. Lance-shaped to ovate-lance-shaped leaves, up to 14 cm long. Green-yellowish flowers, quite fragrant at night, up to 2.4 cm long, grouped in axillar, terminal racemes. Berry-like fruit, blackish in color.

This is a very hardy shrub seen growing in almost wild state around the Acclimatization Garden of La Orotava. It is poisonous for cows and sheep.

It is cultivated in gardens similarly to the other species of the genus described in this book.

Flowering: Spring-summer-autumn.

Propagation: Seeds and stem cutting.

Chamaedorea elegans. General view.

Chamaedorea elegans Mart. [*Collinia elegans* (Mart.) Liebm. ex. Ørst.]. Palmae. Mexico, Guatemala. PARLOR PALM.

Dioecious palm up to 1.80 m tall with a thin trunk, 2.5-3.5 in diameter, ringed. Pinnate, widely lance-shaped leaves, up to 60-100 cm long. Linear to narrowly lanceolate pinnae, up to 20 cm long and 2.5 cm wide. Inflorescences with long peduncles. Female, pale yellow flowers. Male flowers similar to female flowers but having a pistilode instead of a pistil. Globular fruit, black, approximately 6 mm in diameter.

It prefers rich, well-drained

soils. It needs shade and moist conditions.

It is widely cultivated as an indoor plant; it withstands well conditions with little light and humidity frequently found in homes. It is also used in gardens, both alone or in groups.

To obtain seeds it is necessary to plant both sexes together and do a manual pollination.

Propagation: Seeds.

Chamaedora elegans. Inflorescence.

Chamaedorea ernesti-augusti. General view.

Chamaedorea ernesti-augusti. Inflorescence.

Chamaedorea ernesti-augusti H. Wendl. Palmae. Mexico through Honduras.

Dioecious palm with a single trunk, ringed, 2 cm in diameter and with a height of approximately 1.80 m. Leaves widely cuneate-obovate, deeply bifid at the apex, with serrated edges, up to 60 cm long. Inflorescences with long peduncles, almost always standing upright. Orange, small flowers. Berries, ellipsoidal in shape, black and up to 1.5 mm long.

As all the Chamaedorea species it requires shady, damp areas, and it grows best in rich, well-drained soils. This is a very beautiful palm cultivated in gardens either alone or in groups. It is also used as an indoor plant.

Propagation: Seeds.

Chamaerops humilis. General view.

Chamaerops humilis L. Palmae. Mediterranean Sea regions. EUROPEAN FAN PALM.

Dioecious or polygamous-dioecious palm, usually having a shrub-like biotype with several trunks, approximately 1.50 m tall, although at times it acquires the usual palm configuration, reaching heights of up to 6 m. Palmate, green, or often glaucus leaves. Spiny petioles. Blades 60-90 cm wide, deeply divided into seg-

Chamaerops humilis. Flowers and fruit.

ments with only one prominent vein.

This palm withstands the cold very well, up to 9° C below zero. It requires sunny or slightly shady areas. It does not require special soils and its growth process is slow.

The leaves are used to make brooms, hats, among other objects.

It is used to give gardens a tropical air. It is also used to decorate patios, growing in flowerpots.

Propagation: Seeds and sprouts.

63

Chorisia speciosa St. Hil. Bombacaceae. Brazil and Argentina. FLOSS-SILK TREE.

Deciduous tree growing to be 15 m tall. The trunk is wide at the base, spiny and green. Compound, digitated leaves, with 5-7 lanceolate, serrated folioles, up to 12 cm long. Large, beautiful flowers up to 15 cm in diameter. White or yellowish to violet flowers on the higher parts, white or beige on the lower parts, with spots or grooves of the same

Chorisia speciosa. General view.

color as in the higher part. Fruits in oblong capsules, pearshaped, up to 20 cm long, with a large number of seeds. It grows well on most soils as long as it has abundant water. It is somewhat cold resistant and is cultivated on the Mediterranean regions.

Inside the fruit there are hairs resembling cotton used to stuff cushions and pillows. It is used in gardens owing to its beauty.

Flowering: Autumn.
Propagation: Seeds.

Chorisia speciosa. Flower.

Chrysalidocarpus lutescens. General view.

Chrysalidocarpus lutescens. Fruit.

Chrysalidocarpus lutescens H. Wendl. [*Areca lutescens* Bory]. Palmae. Madagascar. YELLOW PALM.

Monocoecious palm with several thin, ringed trunks reaching a height of up to 9 m. Pinnate leaves, 2.25 m long, graciously arched in shape. Yellowish petiole and rachis. Branched inflorescences that appear among the flowers, accompanied by small white or yellowish flowers. Ovoid, yellow fruits, up to 2 cm long.

Although this palm tree can grow in open sunny areas, it prefers shady areas, with rich soil and abundant water. It grows fast.

It is cultivated in tropical and subtropical gardens alone and in groups as natural screens. It is also used in patios and inside homes as a decorating plant in flowerpots. Propagation: Seeds and sprouts.

67

Coccoloba uvifera. General view.

Coccoloba uvifera. Fruit.

Coccoloba uvifera (L.) L. Polygonaceae. The Antilles and tropical America. SEA GRAPE.

Evergreen that usually grows to be 6 m tall, though occasionally it can be seen reaching 12 m. Large leaves, up to 25 cm wide, circular to reniform, glossy, leathery, with prominent red veins. Small, white flowers, very fragrant and growing in racemes up to 30 cm long. Sub-globular fruit purple when ripe, up to 2 cm in diameter, grouped in racemes resembling grape bunches.

It can grow on poor quality soils and withstands drought, the wind and seawater spray.

The fruit is edible and the wood is used in carpentry. This tree is recommended for coastal gardens, and is seen in street alignment and public parks.

Flowering: Spring-summer.
Propagation: Seeds.

Cocos nucifera.
General view.

Cocos nucifera L. Palmae. Melanesia Tropical. COCONUT PALM.

Monocoecious palm with ringed trunk, somehow curved and with a wide base. Pinnate leaves 5-7 cm long. Folioles 90 cm long, green-yellowish in color. Branched inflorescences. White flowers, the female ones up to 2.5 cm in diameter and the male slightly smaller. Large fruits, green-yellowish, with a fibrous mesocarp and containing one seed.

The coconut palm grows well in warm, humid areas, preferably near the coast. It does not require special soils and its growth process is slow. It withstands the marine salt, but is affected by the cold.

This is the most useful palm tree in the world. From its dried endosperm (copra) is obtained coconut oil. The fibers of the mesocarp are used to make rugs, ropes, etc. Sugar and alcohol is made from its sap. The endosperm of the seeds is eaten directly from the fruit. Its milky juice is both drunk as a refreshment and used in the kitchen.

This species is profusely seen in tropical and subtropical gardens, especially those located along the coast. It is usually cultivated in groups. Lately the coconut has been used in sprouting with the first leaves, to be grown as indoor plant.

Propagation: Seeds.

Cocos nucifera. Fruit.

Codiaeum variegatum var. pictum. General view.

Codiaeum variegatum var. pictum. Flowers.

Codiaeum variegatum Blume var. pictum Muell. Arg. [*Croton pictum.* Lodd.] Euphorbiaceae. The Molucca Islands and Malaysia. CROTON.

Evergreen shrub growing to be up to 3.5 m tall. Leathery leaves, with different shapes, sizes and colors. Unisexual flowers, growing in terminal, axillar racemes.

It grows well on most soils as long as they are well drained. The shrubs cultivated in open, sunny areas acquire a greater variety of colors than those growing in the shade. The perfect place for these plants to grow is semishady areas. They need plenty of water.

In the Pacific Islands the natives use the leaves to make some of their clothes. In the Malay Peninsula this plant is used for medicinal purposes.

It is widely used in tropical and subtropical gardens and is very popular as an indoor plant. There are many cultivar.

Propagation: Usually by stem cutting.

73

Coffea arabica. General view.

Coffea arabica. Fruit.

Coffea arabica L. Rubiaceae. Abyssinia, Mozambique and Angola. COFFEE.

Evergreen shrub growing to be up to 4.5 m tall. Ovate-lanceolate leaves, 10-12 cm long, dark green, shiny above and paler beneath. White flowers, clustered in racemes at the axils of the leaves. Small fruit, red when ripe, usually containing two seeds.

Although it can survive in open, sunny areas it prefers semishady regions. It grows best in well-drained, rich soils with abundant water. It grows fast.

It is a very decorative plant, with shiny leaves, white, fragrant flowers which are followed by the red fruits, which are very ornamental.

The seeds are the grains of coffee. Apparently, the coffee plants were taken by the Arabs from Abyssinia to Arabia; today being a species grown on most tropical regions throughout the world.

Flowering: Late spring, summer, autumn.

Propagation: Seeds and stem cutting.

75

Coprosma repens. General view.

Coprosma repens 'Variegata'. Leaves.

Coprosma repens A. Rich. [*C. baueri* T. Kirk. non Endl.]. Rubiaceae. New Zealand. MIRROR PLANT.

Evergreen shrub or small tree up to 7.5 m tall. Thick, ovate or oblong leaves, shiny green above, dull green beneath, up to 11 cm long. Fruit is drupes, obovoid, yellow-orange, up to 9 mm long, grouped in racemes.

The natural habitat of this species is rocky areas where it does not grow taller than 90 cm. It can grow in the shade or in the open and withstands the proximity of the ocean.

It is used in gardening for making hedges, groups and as a solitary plant.

Propagation: Seeds, stem cutting and air layering.

Cordyline australis. General view.

Cordyline australis. Fruit.

Cordyline australis (G. Forst.) Hook. f. [*Dracaena australis* G. Forst.]. Agavaceae. New Zealand. GIANT DRACAENA.

Evergreen tree growing to be 10-12 m tall. Ensiform leaves up to 90 cm long and 6 cm wide, that grow at the ends of the branches in clusters. Small, white, fragrant flowers growing in terminal panicles. Berry-like fruit, whitish, globular, up to 6 mm in diameter.

It does not require special soils and can grow both in the sun and in the shade. It grows slowly.

A very strong fiber is obtained from its leaves.

It is used for indoor decoration and in gardens.

Flowering: Spring-summer.

Propagation: Seeds and stem cutting.

79

Corynocarpus laevigata. General view.

Corynocarpus laevigata. Flowers.

Corynocarpus laevigata J. R. Forst. et G. Forst. Corynocarpaceae. New Zealand. NEW ZEALAND LAUREL.

Evergreen tree reaching 12 m tall. Elliptical-oblong to oblong-obovate leaves, shiny green, up to 18 cm long. Small, greenish or whitish flowers growing in terminal panicles up to 20 cm long. Fruit in drupes, orange in color and fragrant, up to 4 cm long.

It accepts most soils, but prefers sunny areas. It withstands the proximity of the ocean.

The fruit, similar to the medlar, hence its name «fragrant medlar», is edible. The seeds are poisonous.

This is a very ornamental plant, utilized as an alignment tree in streets as well as in gardens in general. Its shape resembles the magnolia plant.

Flowering: Spring.
Propagation: Seeds.

81

Crescentia cujete. General view.

Crescentia cujete. Fruit.

Crescentia cujete L. Bignoniaceae. Tropical America. CALABASH TREE, GÜIRA.

Evergreen or slightly deciduous tree reaching up to 12 m in height. Oblong or oblanceolate leaves up to 24 cm long. Large flowers up to 10 cm long, green-whitish with purple veins and spots; their smell is fetid and grow on the trunk or branches. Fruit up to 40 cm in diameter, globose or oviform, yellow-greenish in color.

It does not require special soils, though it prefers sunny areas. It grows fast and accepts the proximity of the sea. It withstands droughts.

When the pulp and seeds are removed from the fruit, it is used as container, or to make maracas or smoking pipes, owing to the woody mesocarp.

This tree is cultivated in public and private gardens, alone and in groups.

Flowering: Autumn.
Propagation: Seeds and stem cutting.

Cycas revoluta. General view.

Cycas revoluta Thunb. Cycadeceae. Japan. SAGO PALM.

Dioecious plant 2-3 m tall. Erect trunk, topped with a crown of pinnate leaves up to 110 cm long, that give it its palm tree aspect. The folioles are linear-lanceolate, up 10 16 cm long, with acute tips and revolute edges. The male inflorescences are shaped as terminal cones and are 40-50 cm long; the female ones consist of a bunch of carpellary, whitish, extended leaves that start at the apex of the trunk. The ovules are located on its edges. The red, oval seeds are over 4 cm long. This plant prefers rich soils with adequate draining. It can live in the sun but grows better in semishaded areas. It grows slowly.

From the medulla of the trunk is obtained a kind of flour known as «sago» that has become less used because it has cancer-giving properties.

This tree is widely used indoors and in gardens. It is ideal for inside courtyards, and is seen in bonsais.

Propagation: Seeds and sprouts.

Cycas revoluta. Carpellary leaves.

Delonix regia.
General view.

Delonix regia (Bojer) Raf. (Poinciana regia Bojer). Leguminosae. Madagascar. FLAMBOYANT.

Deciduous tree reaching 10-12 m tall, with umbrella-like horizontal branches. Oval, bipinnate leaves up to 40 cm long. Pinnae up to 10 cm long. Oblong folioles, approximately 1 cm long. Dark red to orange-red flowers up to 12 cm in diameter, grouped in corymbiform racemes. The higher petal is white in trees with dark red flowers, and it is yellow in those with red-orange flowers. Fruit in pods up to 60 cm long and 5 cm or more wide.

It accepts most soils as long as they are well drained. It requires sun and does not withstand the wind well. It has a very agressive root system; for this reason it must not be planted near buildings. It can grow near the sea and its growth process is fast.

Its bark has medicinal properties and the seeds are used to make necklaces.

This is one of the most beautiful flower trees seen in tropical regions. It is cultivated in parks, private gardens and in avenues.

Flowering: Spring-summer.

Propagation: Seeds.

Delonix regia. Flowers.

Dombeya X cayeuxii. General view.

Dombeya X cayeuxii. Flowers.

Dombeya X cayeuxii André [*D. bourgessiae X D. wallichii*]. Sterculiaceae.

Evergreen shrub or small tree reaching up to 7 m tall. Alternate, heart-shaped, serrated leaves, sometimes longer than 30 cm, covered with hairs. Pink flowers, grouped in pendular umbels and provided with long peduncles. Pubescent bracts in the umbel, up to 2.5 cm long and 1.25 cm wide Fruits in capsules.

This plant can grow on poor soils and tolerates drought, but it grows best in favorable conditions. It withstands the shade but prefers the sun.

It is very used in gardens, alone and forming groups. Flowering: Autumn-winter. Propagation: Stem cutting.

Erythrina crista-galli. General view.

Erythrina crista-galli L. Leguminosae. Brazil. COCKSPUR CORAL TREE.

Deciduous tree growing to be up to 8 m tall, although it is sometimes a shrub. Spiny branches and petioles. Trifoliate leaves up to 28 cm long. Lanceolate folioles or ovate-lanceolate, the terminal foliole being the largest, up to 16 cm long. Red, cockscombed flowers up to 5 cm long, grouped in dense racemes up to 50 cm long. Fruit in pods, brown, up to 30 cm long.

It prefers light, well-drained

soils. It needs abundant water in the spring and summer. It stands well the cold. In Argentina it is known as «seibo» and its flower is the «national flower». The wood is used for making rafts, cart wheels, etc.

Owing to its beautiful flowers it is cultivated in gardens.

Flowering: Spring-summer-autumn.

Propagation: Seeds.

Erythrina crista-galli. Flowers.

Eucalyptus ficifolia. General view.

Eucalyptus ficifolia. Flowers.

Eucalyptus ficifolia F. J. Muell. Myrtaceae. Australia. RED-FLOWERING GUM.

Evergreen tree being as tall as 9 m. Ovate-lanceolate leaves up to 15 cm long. Flowers in umbels grouped in panicles, in colors that range from white and pink to orange and red. The lobes of the calyx and the petals are joined to form a calyptra. Fruit in capsules, woody, urn-shaped, up to 3.2 cm in diameter and 4.5 long.

It prefers heavy, hardy soil but grows badly on sandy areas. It withstands cold, heat and drought and requires a sunny spot to grow.

It is a very spectacular tree when its flowers blossom. It is used as aligning tree as well as in parks and gardens.

Flowering: Spring-summer-autumn.

Propagation: Seeds.

Eugenia uniflora. General view.

Eugenia uniflora. Fruit.

Eugenia uniflora L. Myrtaceae. Tropical America. SURINAM CHERRY.

Evergreen shrub or small tree up to 6 m tall. Opposite, ovate-lanceolate leaves up to 6 cm long, provided with short petioles, dark green above, paler beneath. Solitary white flowers, about 1.5 cm in diameter, growing on long peduncles. Globose-ovoid fruits, red when ripe and with eight longitudinal grooves.

This tree grows well on most soils although it does best in rich, well-drained terrain, preferably slightly shady. It grows fast and requires adequate watering and fertilizing. It is widely cultivated in tropical regions. The edible fruit is used to make jam, jelly and sherbets.

In gardening it is used alone or for making hedges, as it can be pruned. It can also grow in flowerpots.

Flowering: Several times throughout the year.

Propagation: Seeds.

Euphorbia pulcherrima. General view.

Euphorbia pulcherrima. Flowers.

Euphorbia pulcherrima Willd. ex Klotzsch. [*Poinsettia pulcherrima* (Willd. ex Klotzsch R. C. Grah.] Euphorbiaceae. Mexico and Central America. POINSETTIA.

Deciduous shrub up to 4 m tall. Ovate-ellyptical to lanceolate or panduriform leaves, dentate or lobulated, up to 32 cm long. Very small flowers clustered in ciathiums. The cyathiums are grouped in terminal cymes, resembling umbels, surrounded by lanceolate bracts, as large as the leaves, red in color.

This is a hardy shrub that grows on most soils, though it prefers sunny areas. To obtain better flowers they must be pruned soon after flowering. It grows fast.

It is widely cultivated and there are cultivars with bracts with different tones of red, white and pink.

It is used as a garden shrub, on roadsides, as flower in bunches, in flowerpots and especially at Christmas, when it is very popular and gets a good price.

Flowering: Autumn-winter.
Propagation: Stem cutting.

Feijoa sellowiana. General view.

Feijoa sellowiana O. Berg. Myrtaceae. Southern Brazil, Uruguay, Paraguay and Argentina. FEIJOA.

Evergreen shrub or small tree up to 6 m tall with white-tomentous branches. Ellyptical-oblong, opposite leaves, dark green above, white-tomentous beneath, up to 7.5 cm long. Hermaphrodite flowers, solitary, 3 cm in diameter, with fleshy petals, purple inside and white-tomentous outside. Red stamen. Fruit in berries, oval or oblong, green and coated with a fine, whitish dust, 5 to 7.5 cm long.

It grows well in subtropical, dry regions, with cool weather a part of the year. It prefers loam, rich soils. It stands drought and although it accepts some shade it thrives in the sun.

It is cultivated by its edible, fruit that resembles the pine-apple in taste. The fruits fall down when ripe and must stored in cool places until they are ready to be eaten. They are eaten as they are or are used to make jam, jelly, etc. It is used as a garden plant too.

Flowering: Autumn.
Propagation: Seeds, stem cutting and air layering.

Feijoa sellowiana. Fruit.

Ficus aspera. General view.

Ficus aspera. Fruit.

Ficus aspera G. Forst. [*F. par-cellii* Veitch.]. Moraceae. Pacific Islands. CLOWN FIG.

Evergreen small tree or large shrub. Oblong-oval leaves with asymmetric base, dentated, acuminate, hairy, especially beneath, up to 20 cm long, with irregular dark and light green and cream white spots. Tricolored fruit, green, white and red, 3 cm in diameter.

It prefers well-drained soils and is demanding with the temperature. It grows slowly.

Although it is a very beautiful species it is seldom seen in gardens. It is used as indoor plant.

Propagation: Air layering.

Ficus benjamina. General view.

Ficus benjamina. Fruit.

Ficus benjamina L. Moraceae. India, Southeast Asia, Malay Archipelago and Australia. BENJAMIN TREE.

Evergreen tree resembling a weeping willow, reaching heights of up to 20 m. Ovate-ellyptical, acuminate leaves, 10-12 cm long, glossy. Globose fruits, approximately 1 cm in diameter, red when ripe.

It accepts most soils. It is affected by the cold and the wind. It grows best when soil is damp, and its growth pace is slow.

This tree is adequate for road sides and parks. It is widely used as an indoor plant in flowerpots.

Propagation: Seeds, stem cutting and air layering.

Ficus elastica Roxb. ex Hornem. Moraceae. From Nepal to Assam and Burma. RUBBER TREE.

Evergreen tree up to 30 m tall. Oblong to ellyptical, leathery, shiny leaves, up to 30 cm long, wrapped with involucral, yellowish stipules with pink hues before blooming. Axillar fruits, usually in pairs, oblong ovate, yellow-greenish in color, up to 3 cm long.

Cv. *Variegata,* with pale green leaves and white or yellow edges.

Cv. *Decora,* with larger, wider leaves, dark green and with red stipules.

It prefers sunny, warm areas with abundant water. It is not too demanding concerning the soil and it grows fast.

It has been cultivated in Malaysia and India for extracting its rubber. It was also used as an indoor plant, although it is being substituted by its cultivars.

In gardening it must only be used in parks and squares with enough space for its development. It must not be planted near buildings owing to its aggressive roots.

Propagation: Stem cutting and air layering.

Ficus elastica. Fruit.

Ficus lyrata. General view.

Ficus lyrata. Leaves.

Ficus Lyrata Warb. [*F. pandurata* Hort. Sander, non Hance.]. Moraceae. Tropical Western Africa. FIDDLE-LEAF FIG.

Evergreen tree reaching 12 m tall when cultivated, but being up to 25 m tall when growing in its natural habitat. Large, violin-shaped leaves, coriaceous, shiny above and up to 40 cm long. Globose fruits, up to 5 cm in diameter, purple with white spots when ripe.

It tolerates most soils but prefers rich, well-drained areas, with a high humidity factor. It is affected by the cold.

This is a very decorative species thanks to its large, odd leaves. It is cultivated in gardens and parks and is also used as an indoor plant.

Propagation: Stem cutting and air layering.

Ficus macrophylla. General view.

Ficus macrophylla. Leaves.

Ficus macrophylla Desf. ex Pers. [*F. macrocarpa* Hügel ex Kunth et Bouché]. Moraceae. Australia. MORETONBAY FIG.

Evergreen tree up to 40 m tall although in the Canary Islands it does not grow taller than 15 m. The trunk is gray and the oldest trees show aerial roots. Entire, ovate-elliptical leaves, dark green above, rusty colored beneath, up to 25 cm long, provided with long petioles. The terminal bud of the shoots is over 10 cm long and yellowish in color. Globose, axillar fruit up to 2.5 cm in diameter, purple with paler spots.

It accepts most soils and has some resistance for cold weather conditions. It stands the proximity of the sea.

Owing to its large size it must be cultivated in parks or large gardens. When young it can be used as an indoor plant in flowerpots.

Propagation: Stem cutting.

109

Ficus microcarpa. General view.

Ficus microcarpa L. f. Moraceae. Tropical Asia and Malaysia. LAUREL FIG.

Evergreen tree up to 20 m tall. Ellyptical, glossy leaves, up to 16 cm long. Globose fruits, yellowish or reddish, blackish when matures, up to 1 cm in diameter.

It grows well on most soils, but prefers sunny, damp areas. It can grow near the sea and grows fast. It accepts thorough pruning.

Ficus microcarpa. Fruit.

It is used as aligning tree as well as in parks and gardens. Its powerful roots upraise street pavement and dig into pipes in their search for water, it must therefore be planted away from buildings, unless preventive measures are taken.

Propagation: Stem cutting and air layering.

111

Ficus rubiginosa. General view.

Ficus rubiginosa. Fruit.

Ficus rubiginosa Desf. ex Venten [*F. australis* Willd.]. Moraceae. Australia. RUSTY FICUS.

Evergreen tree that in the Canary Islands reaches heights of 8 to 12 m, whereas its Australian biotype is either a shrub or a large tree. From its branches hang numerous red roots. Leathery, oval or elliptical leaves up to 10 cm long, dark, glossy green above and rusty tomentous beneath. Small, globular fruits with reddish tones, about 1 cm in diameter.

It accepts different kinds of soils but prefers well-drained areas. It stands the vicinity of the sea and its root system is not as penetrating as with other species of Ficus. It is affected by the wind.

It is used as roadside and shade-giving tree. It is also planted indoors, in flowerpots.

Propagation: Stem cutting and air layering.

Ficus sycomorus.
General view.

Ficus sycomorus L. Moraceae. Egypt, Syria, Sudan through South Africa. SYCAMORE FIG.

Evergreen tree, although in the Canary Islands it sheds some of its leaves; it grows to be over 20 m tall. The leaves have long petioles, and are oval or almost orbicular, up to 20 cm long, dark green above, lighter beneath, with hairy veins on this side. Unisexual, tiny flowers, grouped inside fleshy, pyriform receptacles, with only one opening on the apex, forming branched racemes on the trunk and branches, or else alone in the axils of the leaves. The fruit comes in small drupes clustered inside the receptable forming a pyriform infructescence in syconus, up to 3 cm

114

long. The syconus are the figs, densely covered with whitish hair, green-yellowish with red hues in color.

It grows well on most soils but prefers sunny areas. In Africa it grows along the banks of rivers and watercourses, although it can be seen in the plains. It is affected by the cold.

The fruit is edible and is eaten by some African people. It is also eaten by birds, monkeys and other animals. This is the sycamore tree mentioned in the Bible. The wood was used by the Egyptians to make the sarcophagous for their mummies.

Owing to its large size it is only grown in public parks and gardens.

Propagation: Seeds, stem cutting and air layering.

Ficus sycomorus. Fruit.

Ginkgo biloba.
General view.

Ginkgo biloba L. Ginkgoaceae. China. GINKGO. MAIDEN-HAIR TREE.

Deciduous, dioecious tree, up to 35 m tall. Macroblasts with scattered leaves. Brachyblasts with a rosette of flowers in the apexes. Fan-shaped up to 14 cm long, with long petioles, entire or with a cleft in the central part starting at the apex. The male flowers are clustered in amentiform, lax strobiles. The female flowers are in groups of two on long peduncles. Yellowish seeds, resembling drupes, up to 2.5 cm long.

This tree prefers rich, well-drained soils in sunny areas and stands well the cold. It grows slowly.

The Ginkgo is considered as a «Living fossil» for its being the only survivor of an extinct race. The edible seeds are considered delicacies in China and Japan.

It is used as aligning tree in avenues and streets, as well as shade tree in parks and gardens. Only male trees are used, for when the seeds of the female trees fall to the ground release an unpleasant butyric acid smell.

Flowering: Spring.

Propagation: Seeds, stem cutting, air layering and grafting.

Ginkgo biloba. Flowers.

Grevillea banksii. General view.

Grevillea banksii. Flowers.

Grevillea banksii R. Br. Proteaceae. Australia.

Evergreen shrub or small tree reaching up to 6 m tall. Pinnately parted leaves up to 25 cm long. Linear or lanceolate segments, up to 10 cm long, silky-tomentous beneath. Red or sometimes white flowers, clustered in racemes up to 18 cm long.

It prefers well drained soils and sunny areas, for in the shade its flowering decreases. It is affected by limestone and dies in freezing weather. It grows fast.

This shrub is often seen in groups or standing alone. The inflorescences can be used as bouquet flowers.

Flowering: Almost the entire year.

Propagation: Seeds and stem cutting.

Grevillea robusta. General view.

Grevillea robusta. Flowers.

Grevillea robusta A. Cunn. Proteaceae. Australia. GREVILLEA, SILKY OAK.

Evergreen tree raching heights of up to 30 m. although it is usually smaller when cultivated. Pinnate or nearly bipinnate leaves up to 35 cm long, with whitish folioles beneath, resembling the fronds of a fern. Golden yellow flowers clustered in racemes up to 15 cm long. Fruit in folicule, dark brown to blackish in color, up to 18 mm long and with 1 or 2 seeds.

It tolerates most kinds of soils although it requires sunny areas for an adequate flowering. It stands cold weather and drought andgrows fast.

Its good quality wood is used for barrel and cabinet-making. This is a very spectacular tree when it flowers. It is used as aligning tree as well as in parks and gardens. When young it is used as indoor plant.

Flowering: Spring-summer.
Propagation: Seeds and stem cutting.

Greyia radlkoferi. General view.

Greyia radlkoferi. Flowers.

Greyia radlkoferi Szysz. Melianthaceae. South Africa. TRANSVAAL BOTTLEBRUSH.

Deciduous shrub or small tree, although at the Acclimatization Garden of Orotava it does not shed its leaves. The latter are simple, alternate, cordiform to oval, lobated and dentated, up to 25 cm long, dark green above, paler beneath. Scarlet flowers, approximately 2.5 cm long, with long stamens, grouped in racemes at the end of twigs. Fruit in capsules, cylindrical, up to 1.3 cm long.

It requires well-drained soils but once it has grown up it stands the lack of water. It requires sunny regions. When the tree has flowered the racemes with dry flowers must be cut off with some of the twig in order to avoid that in the future the tree turns bare of flowers and leaves.

It is used in gardening either alone or in groups.

Flowering: Autumn-winter-spring.
Propagation: Seeds and stem cutting.

Hibiscus rosa-sinensis Cv. General view.

Hibiscus rosa-sinensis Cv. Flower.

Hibiscus rosa-sinensis L. Malvaceae. Asia. CHINESE HIBISCUS, ROSE-OF-CHINA.

Evergreen shrub that can reach 4 m tall. Oval leaves, dentated on its apical part, up to 15 cm long. Large, red flowers that grow alone at the axils of the leaves. Fruits in capsule.

It prefers rich soils, although it can grow in less favorable conditions. It requires the sun to produce abundant flowers and its growth pace is fast.

The flowers of this tree are used in some countries as a hair dye and for shining shoes. In Hawaii the flowers are used to make necklaces to welcome tourists.

Flowering: Throughout the year.
Propagation: Stem cutting.

Hibiscus schizopetalus. General view.

Hibiscus schizopetalus. Flower.

Hibiscus schizopetalus (M. T. Mast) Hook. f. Malvaceae. Tropical Eastern Africa. JAPANESE HIBISCUS.

Evergreen shrub up to 3 m tall with long, pendular branches. Simple ellyptical-ovate, dentated leaves, up to 16 cm long. Pendular flowers on long peduncles. Petals up to 6 cm long, curved, laciniated and red-pink in color. Fruit in capsules.

It requires rich soils, well-drained and highly humid. It prefers rather shady areas and its growth pace is fast.

It is widely used in gardens in tropical and subtropical countries. It cam be cultivated alone or forming groups. It has also been seen used as a climbing tree to cover a square.

Flowering: Autumn-winter.
Propagation: Stem cutting.

127

Howea belmoreana. General view.

et F. J. Muell.) Becc. Kentia belmoreana C. Moore et F. J. Mueell. Palmae. Lord Howe's Island. BELMOR SENTRY PALM.

Monoecious palm up to 7.9 m tall with ringed trunk. Pinnate leaves, up to 2 m long, very arched and with quite short petioles. Erect pinnae approximately 2.5 cm wide. Flowers in triads (2 male and 1 female), arranged along spikes that sprout alone in the axils of leaves and provided with long peduncles. Ellipsoidal fruits, up to 3.5 cm

Howea belmoreana. Fruit.

long, green-yellowish in color.

This palm prefers loam, rich, well-drained soils. It grows well both in the sun or in shady areas and its growth pace is slow.

It is used for indoor decoration as well as in park and gardens, either alone or in groups. It is also seen growing along streets and avenues.

Propagation: Seeds.

Howea forsteriana. General view.

Howea forsteriana. Inflorescence.

Howea forsteriana (C. Moore et F. J. Muell.) Becc. [*Kentia forsteriana* C. Moore et F. J. Muell.] Palmae. Lord Howe's Island. KENTIA.

Monoecious palm reaching over 18 m tall. Pinnate leaves, up to 3 m long, straight when young and bending with age. Long petioles. Horizontal pinnae or somewhat pendular. The flowers appear in triads along spikes provided with long peduncles. Spikes in groups of 3-6 formed in the axils of the leaves. Ellipsoidal fruits up to 3.5 cm long, green-yellowish in color.

It does not require much concerning the soil, although it prefers loam, rich, well-drained soil. It grows either in the sun or in the shade and it grows fast.

This is one of the most popular palm, widely used for indoor decoration. It is also cultivated in gardens both alone and in groups. It is also used as aligning tree in avenues and streets.

Propagation: Seeds.

131

Iochroma cyaneum. General view.

Iochroma cyaneum. Flowers.

Iochroma cyaneum (Lindl.) M. L. Green. [I. lanceolatum (Miers) Miers; *I. tubulosum* Benth.] Solanaceae. Northwestern South America.

Evergreen shrub up to 3 m tall. Entire, alternate, ovate-lanceolate leaves, up to 20 cm long, acute to acuminate. Tubular flowers provided with long peduncles. The corolla can reach up to 5 cm long, with tones ranging from dark blue to blue-purple. Fruit in berries.

It does not require special soils. It prefers sunny areas although it can live in shaded areas.

It in used in tropical and subtropical gardens and is seen alone and in groups.

Flowering: Almost throughout the year.

Propagation: Seeds and stem cutting.

Jacaranda mimosifolia. General view.

Jacaranda mimosifolia. Flowers.

Jacaranda mimosifolia D. Don. [*J. ovalifolia* R. Br.]. Bignoniaceae. Brazil, Argentina and Uruguay. JACARANDA.

Deciduous tree reaching heights of up to 15 m tall. Compound, bipinnate leaves up to 80 cm long. Oblong-rhomboidal flowers up to 5 cm long, clustered in pendular terminal panicles. Fruit in capsules, flat, suborbicular and up to 7 cm long, holding numerous alate seeds.

It grows on most soils and stands cold weather rather well. It is seen in Mediterranean countries and its growth pace is fast. It requires sunny areas and its wood is appreciated for cabinet-making.

This is a very beautiful tree, especially when it flowers. It is generally used as aligning tree as well as in parks and gardens.

Flowering: Spring-summer.
Propagation: Seeds and stem cutting.

Jubaea chilensis. General view.

Jubaea chilensis. Fruit.

Jubaea chilensis (Mol.) Baill. [*J. spectabilis HBK.*]. Palmae. CHILEAN WINE PALM TREE.

Monoecious palm reaching up to 25 m tall. Very thick trunk, up to 1.8 m in diameter. Pinnate leaves, green or green-greyish, up to 4 m long. Short petioles with smooth edges. Inflorescences measuring over 90 cm in length, brown and appearing among the leaves. Ovoidal, yellow fruits, up to 3.5 cm long.

It accepts most soils but requires sunny areas. It withstands cold weather, even when it gets as cold as −7° C.

The sap is obtained by means of cuts in the trunk. An adult palm can produce as much as 400 liters of sap, which concentrated by boiling becomes the «palm honey», a product commonly seen in the western coast of South America. When the sap is fermented it can be turned into wine.

The fruit of this palm is known as «small coconuts» for their resemblance to regular coconuts and because they are eaten in the same way.

This palm tree is cultivated in parks and gardens in Mediterranean countries.

Propagation: Seeds.

Kigelia africana. General view.

Kigelia africana (Lam.) Benth. Bignoniaceae. Tropical Africa. SAUSAGE TREE.

Semideciduous tree reaching heights of up to 15 m. Imparipinnate leaves 30 cm or more in length. There are usually 7 to 11 elliptical-oblong or obovate folioles, up to 14 cm long. Bell-shaped flowers, blood red in color, up to 10 cm long, clustered in pendular panicles. Elongated, sausage-like fruits, up to 60 cm long, hanging from long peduncles.

This tree accepts most soils and can stand drought up to

Kigelia africana. Fruit.

certain extent. It does not grow well in very cold regions and it grows fast.

When the fruit is crushed or ground it is used for healing skin ulcers, syphilis and rheumatism. The fruit is also baked and added as a flavoring substance in the beer-making process. The wood is utilized to make canoes.

This tree is seen in large gardens and parks as well as in aligning formations.

Flowering: Summer-autumn.

Propagation: Seeds.

Lagunaria patersonii. General view.

Lagunaria patersonii. Flowers.

Lagunaria patersonii (Andr.) G. Don. Malvaceae. Australia, Norfolk Island and Lord Howe's Island. NORFOLK IS-LAND HIBISCUS.

Evergreen tree up to 13 m tall. Entire, oblong or oval-oblong leaves, green-greyish, up to 14 cm long. Bell-shaped flowers, up to 6,5 cm long, resembling hibiscus flowers, pink in color, growing alone or in clusters. Obovoid to ellip-soidal fruit in capsules, up to 4.5 cm long, with a large amount of hairs that irritate the skin.

It requires well-drained soils. It stands the proximity of the ocean and the spray brought by the breeze; for this reason it is an adequate species to grow on coastal plantations. It prefers open, sunny areas and is has some resistance to cold weather. It is used for urban alignment and in gardens in general.

Flowering: Spring-summer.
Propagation: Seeds.

Lantana camara. General view.

Lantana camara. Flowers.

Lantana camara L. Verbenaceae. Tropical America. YELLOW SAGE.

Evergreen shrub 1½-2 m tall, hairy and sometimes thorny. Opposite, ovate to oblong-ovate leaves, dentated-crenulated, up to 11 cm long. Small, yellow-orange to orange turning into red flowers, clustered in axilar and terminal capitulums, up to 3.5 cm in diameter. Fruits in drupes, blackish, approximately 3 mm in diameter.

It does not require much concerning the soil, although it prefers well-drained, rich ground. It requires the sun and grows fast. It must be pruned short if it dries up or if it turns too woody.

This shrub is used for home medicinal purposes.

It is widely used in gardening and can be planted either alone or forming hedges.

Flowering: Almost throughout the year.
Propagation: Seeds and stem cutting.

143

Livistona chinensis var. chinensis. General view.

Livistona chinensis var. chinensis. Fruit.

Livistona chinensis (Jacq.) R. Br. ex Mart. *var chinensis.* Palmae. Japan, China. CHINESE FAN PALM.

Hermaphroditic palm reaching more than 9 m tall. Palmate leaves, up to 3 m long. Pecioles with dentated bases. Limbs divided into many segments with pendular apexes. Branched inflorescences that sprout among the leaves. Hermaphrodite flowers in cincinnus of up to 6 flowers, white in color. Ellipsoidal fruits, green-bluish to green, up to 2 cm long.

It prefers rich soils, well-drained, and very humid. It thrives both in the sun and in shaded areas. It grows slowly.

In China the leaves are used to make fans.

This is a very ornamental palm tree widely used in tropical and subtropical countries. It is seen in parks and gardens and is also used for interior decoration and in courtyards as flowerpot plant. Propagation: Seeds.

Macadamia integrifolia. General view.

Macadamia integrifolia. Fruit.

Macadamia integrifolia Maiden et Betche. Proteaceae. Australia. MACADAMIA NUT.

Evergreen tree that in Australia can reach 18 m tall, but elsewhere rarely surpasses 9 m. When young the leaves are serrated-dentated and when adult they become oblong-lanceolate to obovate, 10-30 cm long. They are grouped in verticils usually made up of three leaves, although occasionally there are four. Whitish, fragrant, hermaphrodite flowers, in racemes up to 30 cm long. Globose fruits up to 3 cm in diameter, with one spherical or two semispherical seeds.

It grows upright, in dry or humid areas. It prefers well-drained soils and it grows slowly.

It is cultivated in tropical and subtropical regions. The seeds are very tasty, and are eaten raw or roasted. The wood is used for cabinet-making.

It is recommended as a shade-giving tree.

Flowering: Several times throughout the year.
Propagation: Seeds and grafting.

147

Mackaya bella. General view.

Mackaya bella. Flower.

Mackaya bella Harv. [*Asystasia bella* Hort.]. Acanthaceae. South Africa. MACKAYA.

Evergreen shrub reaching up to 2 m tall. Opposite, ovate-oblong, sinuated-dentated, acuminate leaves up to 14 cm long. Funnel-shaped, pale lavender flowers, with darker veins, up to 6 cm long, grouped in terminal racemes. Fruit in capsules, elongated, up to 7 cm long.

It needs rich, well-drained soils and prefers shady areas.

It is affected by cold weather and can be grown in coastal gardens.

It is widely used in gardening. It can be planted alone or in groups.

Flowering: Autumn-winter-spring.

Propagation: Seeds and stem cutting.

Mammea americana. General view.

Mammea americana. Fruit.

Mammea americana L. Guttiferae. West Indies and northern South America. MAMEY.

Evergreen tree reaching heights of 20 m. Entire, oblong-obovate, leathery, leaves, shiny above, 20 to 22 cm long, and 10 cm wide. Polygamous flowers, white fragrant, solitary or in clusters in the branches. Globose fruits up to 15 cm in diameter, rusty in color, with 1-4 large seeds.

It prefers rich, well-drained, soils. It is affected by cold weather and can stand the proximity of the sea.

This is a very beautiful tree that resembles the magnolia tree. It is cultivated by the fruits that are similar in flavor to peaches. The fruits are eaten directly from the tree or are used to makes sauces, jams, preserves, etc. In Mexico the juice and seeds are used as insecticides. With the flowers is made a liqueur called «Créme de Créole.» The wood is of good quality.

Fructification: Autumn-winter.
Propagation: Seeds and stem cutting.

Mangifera indica. Cv. General view.

Mangifera indica L. Anacardiaceae. India. MANGO.

Evergreen tree reaching up to 30 m tall, but usually not being this tall. Oblong-lanceolate to elliptical leaves, up to 25-30 cm long, dark green in color. Yellowish or pinkish flowers clustered in panicles. Edible fruits of different size, greenish, yellow or reddish.

It grows well on most soils, although it prefers rich, deep, well-drained ground. It dies in cold, damp weather. It requires warmer weather than the avocado tree and stands better the effects of the wind.

When growing the tree shows a reddish hue which constitutes one of the most attractive characteristics of this tree. De Candolle affirms

152

Mangifera indica. Cv. Fruit.

that this tree has been cultivated by man for over 4000 years. In Indian literature this tree is mentioned and praised.

Selected cultivars such as 'Haden', 'Irwin', 'Keitt', 'Zill', etc., produce a very tasty fruit which is usually eaten straight from the tree, although it is also used to make jams, etc. The unselected cultivars yield a fruit which is fibrous and turpentine like in flavor.

The leaves of the mango are used in Mexico for the cleaning of teeth and to harden gums.

In gardening it is used in gardens and parks as well as in road alignment.

Propagation: Seeds, stem cutting and air layering.

Megaskepasma erythrochlamys. General view.

Megaskepasma erythrochlamys. Flowers.

Megaskepasma erythrochlamys Lindau. Acanthaceae. Venezuela. BRAZILIAN RED-CLOAK.

Evergreen shrub up to 2 m tall. Elliptical to oblong-elliptical leaves with entire or ondulated edges, acuminate apex and cuneate base, up to 30 cm long. White or light pink flowers, grouped in terminal spikes up to 20 cm long. Red-purple, ovate to ovate-lanceolate bracts up to 4 cm long. Fruit in capsules.

It prefers well-drained soils, rich in organic matter. It can be cultivated in the sun, but it flowers best in semishady areas. It is affected by drought.

It is mainly cultivated in tropical and subtropical regions. It grows alone or in groups.

Flowering: Autumn-winter.
Propagation: Stem cutting.

155

Microcoelum weddellianum. General view.

Microcoelum weddellianum. Fruit.

Lytocaryum weddellia-num (H. Wendl.) Toledo [Microceolum weddellianum (H. Wendl.) H. E. Moore; Cocos weddelina H. Wendl.] Palmae. Brazil. WEDDEL'S PALM.

Monoecious palm with a long, slender trunk, up to 5 cm in diameter and 3 m tall. Pinnate leaves up to 1.20 m long. Narrowly linear pinnae up to 25 cm long and up to 8 mm long, glaucous beneath. Spineless petioles. The inflorescences appear among the flowers in simple ramification patterns, up to 90 cm long, provided with small unisexual flowers. Ovoid fruits up to 2.5 cm long.

It prefers rich, well-drained soils, partly shady. It grows slowly.

This species is extensively cultivated as flowerpot plant. In gardening it is used alone or in groups.

Propagation: Seeds.

157

Nandina domestica. General view.

Nandina domestica. Flowers.

Nandina domestica Thunb. Berberidaceae. India through Eastern Asia. HEAVENLY BAMBOO.

Evergreen shrub up to 2.5 m tall with thin, bamboo-like shoots. Compound bi or tripinnate leaves up to 55 cm long. Oval or lanceolate folioles up to 5.5 cm long. Small, white flowers clustered in terminal panicles up to 30 cm or more long. Fruit in berries, red, up to 6 mm in diameter.

It grows well in both the sun and shade. It requires well-drained, quite humid soils. It grows slowly and stands cold weather. This is a very nice plant whose foliage turns red in the autumn. It can grow alone or in groups, and it is often growing indoors.

Flowering: Several times in the year.
Propagation: Seeds and stem cutting.

Nerium oleander. Cv. General view.

Nerium oleander. Cv. Flowers.

Nerium oleander L. [*N. indi-cum* Mill.]. Apocynaceae. Mediterranean countries. COMMON OLEANDER.

Evergreen shrub up to 4.5 m tall. Lance-shaped leaves, up to 25 cm long, usually three per verticil. Pink flowers, clustered in terminal compound cymes. Fruit in difolicle up to 17.5 cm long.

It grows on most soils and stands well cold weather, drought and the proximity of the sea. It prefers sunny areas.

This is a very poisonous plant, although its sap has been used to treat some skin diseases.

This tree has been cultivated throughout history as a decorating indoor plant as well as in gardening in general.

There are several cultivars with simple, semidouble and double flowers in white, yellow, pink and red among other colors.

Flowering: Spring-summer-autumn.
Propagation: Seeds and stem cutting.

161

Nuxia floribunda. General view.

Nuxia floribunda. Flowers.

Nuxia floribunda Benth. Loga-niaceae. Tropical Africa and South Africa. WHITE ELDER TREE.

Evergreen up to 18 m tall, although at times it is a shrub. Three leaves per verticil, or, sometimes, or, opposite, widely lanceolate, oblong or oval, entire or slightly ser-rated, up to 16 cm long, with long petioles. Small, tubular, white flowers with exserted stamens, grouped in terminal panicles. Fruit in capsules, oval, small.

It prefers areas with mild winters and quite humid. It does not require special soils and it grows fast. It stands cold weather.

The wood is used for fences and the bark is rich in tannins. This is a very beautiful tree, cultivated in private gardens, parks, and on streets and avenues.

Flowering: Autumn-winter.

Propagation: Seeds and stem cutting.

163

Ochna serrulata. General view.

Ochna serrulata. Fruits.

Ochna serrulata (Hochst.) Walp. Ochnaceae. South Africa. MICKEY-MOUSE PLANT.

Evergreen shrub up to 1.5 m tall. Narrowly elliptical leaves, acutely serrated, dark green above, paler beneath, up to 8 cm long. Flowers growing alone or in racemes, with green-yellowish sepals that turn red in the fruit. Yellow petals that are soon shed. Fruit in pluridrupes in a widened, red receptacle.

It needs loam, rich, well-drained and very damp soils for a fast growing process. It needs the sun.

This shrub is seen in tropical and subtropical gardens. It is planted alone and in groups.

Flowering: Spring.

Propagation: Seeds and stem cutting.

Odontonema callistachyum. General view.

Odontonema callistachyum. Flowers.

Odontonema callistachyum (Schlechtend. et Cham.) O. Kuntze. Acanthaceae. Mexico and Central America.

Evergreen shrub up to 4.5 m tall. Opposite, sinuated, oblong to elliptical-ovate leaves up to 30 cm long. Pink to red flowers up to 3.5 cm long, clustered in raceme-like panicles, up to 45 cm long. Fruit in capsules.

It prefers well-drained soils rich in organic matter. It grows well in both the sun and shade. It is affected by drought. As it ages it becomes bare of leaves and for this reason it must be pruned short.

It is a very ornamental species that can grow alone or in groups.

Flowering: Almost all the year.
Propagation: Stem cutting.

Odontonema strictum. General view.

Odontonema strictum. Flowers.

Odontonema strictum (Nees) O. Kuntze. Acanthaceae. Central America.

Evergreen shrub up to 1.8 m tall. Opposite, oblong, often undulate leaves, acuminate, up to 25 cm long. Scarlet, tubular flowers up to 3 cm long, clustered in raceme-like terminal panicles up to 40 cm long. Fruit in capsules.

It prefers rich, well-drained soils. It is affected by drought and although it accepts the sun directly it grows better in partly shady areas. If it sheds all its lower leaves is must be pruned short.

It is cultivated alone or forming groups.

Flowering: Almost all the year.
Propagation: Stem cutting.

Pandanus utilis. General view.

Pandanus utilis. Fruit.

Pantanus utilis Bory. Pandanaceae. Madagascar. COMMON SCREW PINE.

Dioecious tree reaching heights of up to 18 m. From the lower parts of the trunk spring crutch-like aerial roots. Glaucous, sword-like leaves up to 1.40 m long and 10.5 cm wide, with spiny borders, arranged in rosettes at the end of the branches. Male, spadiciform inflorescences. Female inflorescences in capitula. The yellow-orange fruits come in drupes up to 4.5 cm long, grouped in globose (syncarp) infructescence, up to 25 cm in diameter.

It grows on most soils but prefers warm weather near the sea. It accepts the sun and shade equally well.

The fruit is edible and a fiber to make ropes, hats, baskets, and other objects is obtained from the leaves and roots. This is a very ornamental species generally seen in tropical and subtropical gardens. It is also seen indoors as a decorative plant in flowerpots.

Flowering: Spring.

Propagation: Seeds and shoots.

171

Parkinsonia aculeata. General view.

Parkinsonia aculeata. Flowers.

Parkinsonia aculeata L. Leguminosae. Tropical America. PARKINSONIA. JERUSALEM THORN.

Deciduous tree that can grow as much as 8 m tall, with a characteristic green trunk branches and spines up to 3 cm long. Compound, bipinnate leaves up to 40 cm or more long, with 2-3 pairs of pinnae joined to a very short rachis ending in a thorn. Very small folioles, oblong to obovate. Fuit in pods, light brown, up to 10 cm long.

It accepts most soils and direct contact with the sun. It withstands droughts well and its growth pace is fast.

The foliage and fruit is given as food to cattle.

This is an ornamental tree seen in parks and gardens as well as in urban alignment. It is also used to form hedges.

Flowering: Spring through autumn.

Propagation: Seeds and stem cutting.

Pavonia sepium. General view.

Pavonia sepium. Flowers.

Pavonia sepium St.-Hill. Malvaceae. South America.

Evergreen shrub up to 2.5 m tall. Ovate to oblong-ovate, cuneate, serrated, acuminate, hairy leaves, up to 20 cm long. Yellow, solitary flowers that sometimes have the petals apically joined. Sepals and involucral bracts up to 9 mm long. Petals up 12-18 mm long. Fruit in schizocarps, with five mericarps provided with three erect thorns.

It prefers light, well-drained soils rich in organic matter. It requires a partly shady area to grow well. It grows fast. This shrub is used in tropical and subtropical gardens and it can be planted alone or in groups.

Flowering: Almost throughout the year.

Propagation: Seeds and stem cutting.

Persea americana 'Hass'. General view.

Persea americana Mill. [*P. gratissima* C. F. Gaertn.]. Lauraceae. Tropical America. AVOCADO TREE.

Evergreen tree reaching as tall as 18 m tall and more. Oblong-lanceolate or elliptical-lanceolate to ovate or obovate leaves up to 25 cm long or more. Small, greenish flowers clustred in axilar or terminal panicles. Fleshy, large, piriform fruit in drupes, ovoidal or spherical, green, brown or purple in color, with a large seed.

Var. americana. This is the typical variety whose leaves do not release an anise scent when crushed. This variety includes the Antillean and Guatemalan races.

Var. drymifolia (Schlechtend. et Cham.) S. F. Blake. The leaves of this variety release anise scent when crushed. This variety includes the Mexican race.

This species prefers deep, rich well-drained soils. It does not accept heavy, humid soils. It stands cold weather more than the mango tree. Its twigs are brittle, and for this reason

176

Persea americana 'Fuerte'. Fruit.

it grows better in areas protected from the wind.

The avocado tree is cultivated for its fruit in several parts of the world, such as in Mexico, Central and South America, The West Indies, Hawaii, Israel, Florida, California, India, the Canary Islands, Granada (Spain), etc. The avocado contains abundant vegetal oil, as well as an important number of proteins, vitamins and minerals, all of which make it into an important element in nutrition. It is eaten straight from the tree, in salads and in many varied ways. There are several cultivars which produce its fruits in different times of the year, such as those of 'Fuerte' and 'Hass.'

It is used as a shade and fruit tree in private gardens.

Propagation: Seeds and grafting.

Phoenix dactylifera. General view.

Phoenix dactylifera. Fruit.

Phoenix dactylifera L. Palmae. Arabia and northern Africa. DATE PALM.

Dioecious palm with slender trunk, reaching over 30 m tall. It keeps for many years the sheaths of the leaves that have fallen. Pinnate, glaucous, green grayish leaves, up to 6 m long. The inflorescences appear among the leaves with small, yellowish flowers. Fruit (dates) in drupes, cylindrical to oblong-ellipsoidal, edible, up to 7.5 cm long.

It grows well on most soils and stands periods of drought. It requires the sun and grows fast. It can easily stand temperatures as cold as −9° C without being harmed.

Dates constitute one of the staple food elements in North African and Arabian countries. The main producers are Egypt, Iran and Iraq.

The date palm tree is also used for decoration purposes, growing in parks, gardens and in streets.

Propagation: Seeds and shoots.

179

Phoenix reclinata. General view.

Phoenix reclinata Jacq. Palmae. Tropical Africa. SENEGAL DATE PALM.

Dioecious palm with multiple trunks that start from the base and reaching 7.5 m tall and more. Pinnate, gracefully arched leaves up to 3.5 m long. Orange, spiny petioles. Lanceolate pinnae, up to 70 cm long and 2.5 cm wide, acuminate. The inflorescences arise among the leaves, up to 1.5 m long, provided with unisexual, yellowish flowers. Oblong-ellipsoidal, red-orange to black fruits, up to 1.8 cm long.

It is not too demanding

concerning the soil and prefers sunny areas. It grows fast and can safely stand temperatures as cold as −7° C.

With the sap of this palm an alcoholic beverage is made in Africa. The fibers of the trunks are used to make brushes and brooms. The core of the leave crowns is eaten by African natives.

It is used in gardening alone and to make screens and hedges.

Propagation: Seeds and shoots.

Phoenix reclinata. Fruit.

Phoenix roebelinii. General view.

Phoenix roebelinii. Flowers.

Phoenix roebelenii O'Brien. Palmae. Laos. PYGMY DATE PALM.

Dioecious palm with a thin, alone or multiple trunk 1.8 m tall and more. Pinnate leaves up to 1.2 m long. Narrowly lanceolate pinnae up to 35 cm long and up to 1.3 cm wide. The inflorescences grow among the leaves, up to 80 cm long, with yellowish, unisexual flowers. Blakish fruits, up to 1.2 cm long.

It prefers rich, very damp soils. It requires partly shady areas, although it admits direct contact with the sun. It grows slowly and can withstand temperatures as low as −7° C without problems.

This is a very ornamental palm, used as indoor plant in courtyards. It is also used in gardens, either alone or forming groups.

Propagation: Seeds.

183

Phytolacca dioica. General view.

Phytolacca dioica. Fruit.

Phytolacca dioica L. Phytolaccaceae. South America. OMBÚ.

Dioecious tree with persistent or semipersistent leaves, reaching heights of up to 20 m. It has a very thick trunk, wider at the base. Elliptical or ovate leaves, 25 cm long or more. Unisexual flowers, clustered in suberect or pendular racemes, up to 15 cm long. Fleshy, yellowish fruit.

It accepts most soils and stand strong winds. It accepts the proximity of the sea and it grows fast.

The ombú is greatly appreciated in Argentina, where it often appears in the lyrics of popular songs. Its roots have medicinal properties.

It is used as a shade tree. When used as street aligning tree its powerful roots may uplift the pavement.
Flowering: Spring-summer.
Propagation: Seeds.

185

Psidium guajava. General view.

Psidium guajava. Fruit.

Psidium guajava L. Myrta- COMMON GUAVA.

Evergreen shrub or small tree up to 9 m tall. Scaly brown bark. Quadrangular twigs. Ovate to oblong-elliptical leaves, up to 15 cm long, with prominent veins beneath. White, single flowers or in small groups, up to 3 cm in diameter. Fruit in berries, ovoid to piriform, yellow when ripe.

It does not need special soils, and it requires sunny areas. It stands droughts well. The common guava is cultivated for its fruits in India, Brazil, Guyana, Cuba and in some areas in Florida. Its contents of vitamin C is from two to three times that of oranges. It is eaten straight from the tree and it is used to make preserves, jams, juices and guava paste. The wood is used in carpentry.

It can also be used as ornamental tree in parks and gardens.

Fructification: Autumn-winter-summer.
Propagation: Seeds, stem cutting and grafting.

Rhapis excelsa. General view.

Rhapis excelsa. Inflorescence.

Rhapis excelsa (Thunb.) A. Henry. [*R. flabelliformis* L'Hér. ex Ait.]. Palmae. Southern China. BAMBOO PALM.

Dioecious palm with multiple shoots reaching 3 m tall, covered with a thick brown fiber. Palmate leaves, split almost as far as the base in 3 to 10 linear segments, with serrated margins and truncated, dentated apex, up to 34 cm long and 6 cm wide. The inflorescences appear among the flowers, with small unisexual flowers. Globose to ovoid fruits.

It does not require special soils and prefers partly shady areas, although it can accept sunny regions. It withstands cold weather to temperatures of up to −8° C.

This is a very decorative palm used as indoor plant growing in flowerpots. It is also cultivated in courtyards and gardens to form groups and hedges.

Propagation: Seeds and division.

189

Roystonea regia (HBK) O. F. Cook. [*Oroedoxa regia* HBK.]. Palmae. Cuba. CUBAN ROYAL PALM.

Monoecious palm reaching heights of 20 m or more, with an even, white-greyish trunk, uniformly thick, and very often widened at the base, becoming gradually slender as far as the middle section where it widens, to again start to decrease in thickness as it gets closer to the apex. Pinnate, arched leaves, up to 3 m long, with the folioles joined to the rachis in several levels to form an almost globose crown. Very branched inflo-

Roystonea regia.
Leaves.

rescences. Unisexual, white flowers. Dark red to purple fruits, nearly globose to obovoid, up to 12 mm long.

It is very affected by cold weather. It grows fast in rich, damp soils. It withstands the wind and the saline spray from the sea.

In Cuba the fruit is used to feed cattle. The trunk and leaves are used to build cabins.

This palm is widely used for urban alignment as well as in gardens in tropical and subtropical gardens. It is a species recommended for protected coastal gardens.

Propagation: Seeds and cuttings.

Schinus molle. General view.

Schinus molle L. Anacardia-ceae. Peruvian Andes. PEPPER TREE.

Dioecious, evergreen tree up to 15 m tall, with pendular branches that make it resemble the weeping willow. Compound, pinnate leaves up to 25 cm long. Linear-lanceolate folioles up to 5 cm long. Unisexual, white-yellowish, small flowers, clustered in panicles. Fruit in drupes, spherical, pink to red, up to 7 mm in diameter.

It grows on most soils as long as they are not too

Schinus molle. Fruit.

humid. It requires sunny areas and stands drought. It grows fast.

The seeds are hot in flavor, similar to pepper. It has been used to replace pepper, hence its name. The resin is used in South America as chewing gum. The Peruvian indians prepare a beverage known as «Chicha de molle.»

It is widely used in gardening. It can be seen in squares, parks, as well as in streets and roads.

Flowering: Almost throughout the year.

Propagation: Seeds and cuttings.

Schinus terebinthifolius. General view.

Schinus terebinthifolius. Fruit.

Schinus terebinthifolius Raddi. Anarcadiaceae. Brazil. BRAZILIAN PEPPER TREE.

Dioecious, evergreen or semievergreen shrub or tree, up to 10 m tall. Imparipinnate leaves up to 40 cm long, with 5-19 folioles. Oblong, serrated folioles up to 8 cm long. Unisexual, small, white-greenish flowers clustered in panicles. Fruit in drupes, spherical, red and up to 5 mm in diameter.

This species accepts most soils as long as they are not too humid. It requires sunny areas and withstands drought. It grows fast.

The foliage and fruits are used to make Christmas wreaths. The resin was formerly used to make the «Mission Balsam».

This is a very ornamental tree cultivated in parks, gardens and used for urban street alignment.

Flowering: Spring-summer.

Propagation: Seeds and stem cutting.

Sparmannia africana. Cv. Flore Pleno. General view.

Sparmannia africana. Cv. Flore Pleno. Flower.

Sparmannia africana L. F. Tiliaceae. South Africa. AFRICAN HEMP.

Evergreen small tree or shrub up to 6 m tall. Semi-woody, green, hairy twigs. Cordate-ovate, hairy, acuminate, lobeless leaves that can also be palmatilobate or angular. Long petioles up 23 cm long. Blades up to 28 cm long and 24 cm wide. Flowers with white petals clustered in umbels.

The cultivar «Flore Pleno» produces double flowers.

This plant accepts most soils, and prefers shaded or semishaded areas. It grows fast and is affected by cold weather.

The wood produces a fiber known as African hemp which is not of very good quality. The leaves may irritate the skin.

It is a very decorative tree when it flowers. It is used in gardens, both alone and in groups.

Flowering: Winter.
Propagation: Seeds and stem cutting.

197

Spathodea campanulata. General view.

Spathodea campanulata. Flowers.

Spathodea campanulata Beauv. Bignoniaceae. Tropical Africa. TULIP TREE.

Evergreen tree that in the Canary Islands sheds its leaves once a year, reaching heights of up to 20 m. Pinnate leaves up to 65 cm long, with ovate-lanceolate folioles, up to 12 cm long. Large, bell-like flowers up to 7 cm in diameter, scarlet with gold-yellow edge, clustered in terminal racemes. Fruit in oblong-lanceolate capsules, 15-20 cm long.

It grows well on most soils and stands drought. In rich soils with abundant water it grows fast. It requires contact with the sun to flower adequately. It is affected by freezing weather.

This is one of the most beautiful tropical trees. Before the flowers open they are filled with water; for this reason the tree is also known as the «fountain tree.» Wild Canarian birds pierce the buds of trees and drink the water. This is an adequate tree for street and avenue alignment. It is also widely grown in public and private parks and gardens.

Flowering: Almost throughout the year.

Propagation: Seeds, stem cutting and shoots.

Syzygium jambos. General view.

Syzygium jambos. Fruit.

Syzygium jambos (L.) Alston. [*Eugenia jambos* L.]. Myrtaceae. Southeast Asia. ROSE APPLE.

Evergreen tree reaching heights between 9-12 m. Lanceolate, opposite leaves, shiny green above, paler beneath, up to 18 cm long. Very short petioles. White-greenish flowers up to 8 cm in diameter, with many long stamens that constitute the most striking part of this tree. The flowers are grouped in racemes with not too many flowers. Ovoid, yellow-creamish fruit, with rose-like scent, up to 4 cm long.

This tree prefers loam, well-drained, damp soils, and it needs sunny areas.

Although the fruit is edible it is rather tasteless. It is used to make jams and candies. The wood is of good quality and the bark is used in dying and tanning.

This is the tree of the good and bad which in the Bible had the fruits of immortality.

It is used as a decorative, shade-giving tree in parks and gardens.

Flowering: Spring-summer-autumn.
Propagation: Seeds and stem cutting.

Tecoma alata. General view.

Tecoma alata. Flowers.

Tecoma alata DC. [*T. smithii* W. Wats]. Bignoniaceae.

Evergreen shrub reaching heights of up to 3 m. Imparipinnate, compound leaves with 11-17 oblong, acute, serrated folioles up to 3.2 cm long. Yellow flowers with reddish hues, tubular-infundibuliform, up to 5 cm long, clustered in panicles up to 20 cm long. Fruit in brown linear capsules up to 10 cm long. It does not require special soils and grows best in sunny areas. It must be well watered during the summer. It is affected by cold weather.

It is used in gardening, both alone and forming groups.

Flowering: Almost the entire year.
Propagation: Seeds and stem cutting.

203

Tecoma stans. General view.

Tecoma stans. Flowers.

Tecoma stans (L.) HBK. [*Bignonia stans* L.]. Bignoniaceae. West Indies and from Mexico to Peru. YELLOW BIGNONIA. YELLOW ELDER. TREE.

Evergreen shrub up to 6 m tall. Imparipinnate leaves with 5-11 folioles up to 10 cm long, lanceolate to ovate-oblong, serrated. Yellow, bell-like flowers, 5 cm long, grouped in racemes. Fruit in linear capsules, 20 cm long and 6 mm wide. Alate seeds. It grows on most soils. It is more attractive if is pruned short. It prefers sunny areas and grows fast.

When it flowers it is a very beautiful tree. It is widely used in gardens both alone and in groups.

Flowering: Almost throughout the entire year.
Propagation: Seeds and stem cutting.

Terminalia catappa. General view.

Terminalia catappa. Fruit.

Terminalia catappa L. Combretaceae. Malay Peninsula. TROPICAL ALMOND.

Deciduous tree reaching heights averaging 18-24 m. Its branches are horizontally spreaded. Entire, alternate, aboyate leaves up to 30 cm long, clustered at the end of young branches. Before the leaves fall they become red, lending the tree a very nice aspect. Whitish, small flowers growing in terminal spikes up to 18 cm long. The almond-like fruits are 5-7 cm long, green with pale brown hues when ripe. Edible seeds.

This is a very rustic tree adequate for gardens near the sea for its endurance to the effects of the sea and its breeze.

The seeds are eaten raw and roasted, and from then an almond-like oil is obtained. The green fruit is used to obtain tannin. The wood is used in construction.

This tree is used in street alignment as well as in coastal gardens. It is a beautiful garden tree.

Flowering: Spring-summer-autumn.
Propagation: Seeds.

Tipuana tipu. General view.

Tipuana tipu. Flowers.

Tipuana tipu (Benth.) O. Kuntze. Leguminosae. Southern Brazil to Bolivia. ROSEWOOD. TIPA.

Briefly deciduous tree that may reach heights of up to 30 m. Imparipinnate leaves 30 cm or more long. Folioles in 6-11 pairs, elliptical, obovate or oblong, up to 6 cm long and up to 2 cm or more wide, emarginate. Yelloworange flowers, clustered in axilar racemes shorter than the leaves. Fruit in alate pods, up to 8.5 cm long.

It prefers rich, well-drained soils and it requires sunny areas. It withstands drought and grows fast. It can be transplanted without problems when adult.

The wood of this tree, known as rosewood is used for making cabinets. The bark is used in tanning and home medicine. The foliage is used as fodder.

This tree is cultivated as shade-giving tree, in parks and gardens, as well as for street alignment.

Flowering: Spring-summer.
Propagation: Seeds.

209

Trachycarpus fortunei. General view.

Trachycarpus fortunei. Inflorescence.

Trachycarpus fortunei (Hook.) H. Wendl. Palmae. Northern Burma and Central-eastern China. WINDMILL PALM.

Polygamous - monoecious palm up to 12 m tall. Slender trunk covered with brown fibers produced from the sheaths of old leaves. The fibers are loose and undulate. Fan-like, dark green or sometimes, glaucous leaves. Blades 50-80 cm long, divided into several narrow segments to their middle part, and often to the base. Petioles up to 110 cm long, with toothed borders. Small, yellow flowers clustered in panicular inflorescences up to 60 cm long. Kidney-like fruit, blue when ripe, up to 12 mm long.

It stands well cold weather to temperatures as cold as −11° C. It grows well on most soils as long as they are well-drained and rich.

The fibers are used to make ropes and thick weaves.

It is used in gardening and as an indoor plant.

Propagation: Seeds.

Trithrinax acanthocoma. General view.

Trithrinax acanthocoma. Fruit.

Trithrinax acanthocoma Drude. Palmae. Southern Brazil.

Hermaphroditic palm up to 4.5 m tall, with the trunk covered by a fibrous tissue. The sheaths of leaves are provided with long thorns on the borders. Palmate, orbicular leaves, glaucous beneath, up to 1.8 m long, divided in approximately 40 bifid segments. Thornless petioles up to 90 cm long. The inflorescences appear among the leaves, paniculate, with small flowers. Globose, yellow-creamish fruits up to 2.5 cm in diameter.

It grows on most soils, and prefers sunny areas. It grows slowly and is rather resistant against cold weather.

It is used in gardening thanks to its ornamental aspect.

Propagation: Seeds.

*Washingtonia
filifera.*
General view.

Washingtonia filifera (L. Linden) H. Wendl. Palmae. California, S.W. United States, Mexico. DESERT FAN PALM.

Hermaphroditic palm reaching heights of up to 24 m when growing wild, but not taller than 15 m when it is cultivated. Massive, greyish trunk. Palmate leaves. Plano-convex petioles above, with spiny edges to half or a little further,

up to 1.5 m long. Grey-green blades up to 2 m in diameter, divided into numerous erect segments covered with many threadlike, white fibers. Branched inflorescences with pendular branches that appear among the leaves. Small, white flowers. Ovoid, small, brown fruit in drupes.

This is a very rustic palm that grows fast if given plenty

of water. It prefers sunny areas and withstands the proximity of the sea.

The natives of the places where this palm grows originally used the leaves to make cabins, sandals and baskets. The petioles were used to make furniture and similar objects. The medulla of the spadix was used to make fire by friction and the fruits were used as food.

This palm is used in urban alignment as well as in parks and gardens.

Propagation: Seeds.

Washingtonia filifera. Inflorescence.

Washingtonia robusta H.
Wendl. [*W. sonorae* S. Wats;
W. gracilis S. Parisch.]. Pal-
mae. Mexico. THREAD PALM.

Hermaphroditic palm ave-
raging heights of over 25 m,
with the trunk not as thick as that
of *W. filifera*. Palmate leaves.

Concave petioles above with
spiny edges as far as the ends,
and up to 1.5 m long. Bright
green blades up to 1.8 m
in diameter, divided into many
gracefully arched segments,
without threadlike fibers,
except for the young palms.
Branched inflorescences with
pendular branches that ap-

pear among the leaves. White flowers. Ovoid, small, brown fruit in drupes.

It grows on most soils and requires direct contact with the sun. If provided with abundant water it grows fast.

Its leaves were used in funerals.

It is used as alignment tree in streets as well as in gardening in general.

Propagation: Seeds.

Washingtonia robusta. Inflorescence.

Yucca aloifolia. General view.

Yucca aloifolia. Flowers.

Yucca aloifolia L. Agavaceae. West Indies, Southeast United States and Mexico. YUCCA. SPANISH BAYONET.

Tree with single or multiple trunk, up to 7 m tall. Leaves arranged in rosettes, thick, fleshy, dagger-like, 75 cm long and 6 cm wide, with a thorn at the end. Inflorescences in panicles up to 60 cm long, with white, fragrant flowers about 5 cm long. Black fruit in berries.

This is a very rustic palm, growing well on most soils. It requires little water and withstands the proximity of the sea. It prefers sunny areas.

It is very widely used in gardening, where it is seen growing in lawns, etc.

Flowering: Spring-summer-autumn.

Propagation: Seeds and stem cutting.

219

BIBLIOGRAPHY

BIBLIOGRAPHY

BAILEY, L. H.: *The Standard Cyclopedia of Horticulture*, 3 vols., 3639 p., The MacMillan Company, Nueva Yor, 1947.

BURKART, A.: *Las Leguminosas Argentinas Silvestres y Cultivadas*, 569, p., ACME AGENCY, Soc. de Resp. Ltda., Buenos Aires, 1952.

CEBALLOS, L., y RUIZ DE LA TORRE, J.: *Árboles y arbustos de la España peninsular*, 512 p., Instituto Forestal de Investigaciones y Experiencias y Escuela T. Superior de Ingenieros de Montes, Madrid, 1971.

CHITTENDEN, F. J. (Ed.): *The Royal Horticultural Society Dictionary of Gardening*, 3 vols., 2316 p., Oxford University Press, Oxford, 1977.

CHITTENDEN, F. J. (Ed.): *Supplement to the Royal Horticultural Society Dictionary of Gardening*, 1088 p., Oxford University Press, Oxford, 1979.

FONT QUER, P.: *Diccionario de botánica*, 1244 p., Editorial Labor, S. A. Barcelona, 1977.

GRAF, A. B.: *Exotica 3. Pictorial Cyclopedia of Exotic Plants*, 1834 p., Roehrs Company, E. Rutheford, 1970.

GRAF, A. B.: Tropica. Color Cyclopedia of Exotic Plants and Trees, 1136 p., Roehrs Company, E. Rutheford, 1981.

GUÍNEA LÓPEZ, E., y VIDAL BOX, C.: *Parques y jardines de España. Árboles y arbustos*, 413 p., Publicaciones del Ministerio de Educación y Ciencia, Madrid, 1969.

HOYOS, J.: *Flora tropical ornamental*, 430 p., Sociedad de Ciencias Naturales La Salle. Monografía n.° 24, Caracas, 1978.

KUCK, L. E., y TONGG, R. C.: *The Modern Tropical Garden*, 250 p., Tongg Publishing Company, Honolulú, 1970.

KUNKEL, G.: *Flowering Trees in Subtropical Gardens*, 346 p., Dr. W. Junk b.v., Publishers, La Haya, 1978.

LIBERTY HYDE BAILEY HORTORIUM: *Hortus Third*, 1290 p., MacMillan Publishing Co., Inc., Nueva York, 1978.

MECURRACH, J. C.: *Palms of the World*, 290 p., Harper and Brothers, Nueva York, 1960.

MENNINGER, E. A.: *Flowering Trees of the World*, 336 p., Hearthside Press Incorporated, Nueva york, 1962.

MOORE, H. E.: *The Major Groups of Palms and Their Distribution*, 115 p., L. H. Bailey Hortorium, Nueva York, 1973.

PALMER, E., y PITMAN, N.: *Trees of Southern Africa*, 3 vols., 2235 p., A. A. Balkema, Ciudad del Cabo, 1972.

PAÑELLA BONASTRE, J.: *Árboles de jardín*, 300 p., Oikos-tau, S. A. Ediciones, Barcelona, 1972.

VAN DER SPUY, U.: *South African Shrubs and Trees for the Garden*, 215 p., Hugh Keartland Publishers, Johannesburgo, 1971.

WHITMORE, T. C.: *Palms of Malaya*, 129 p., Oxford University Press, Oxford, 1979.

WRIGLEY, J. W., y FAGG, M.: *Australian Native Plants*, 448 p., Williams Collins Publishers Pty Ltd, Sidney, 1979.

GLOSSARY OF BOTANICAL TERMS

Above.—Upper side of leaves, opposite of beneath.

Aculeate, a.—Provided with prickles.

Acuminate, a.—Ending in a point.

Acute, a.—Any foliaceous organ (leaves, folioles, etc.) narrowed gradually and making an angle of less than 90.

Achene.—Dry fruit, indeshicent, monospermous.

Alkaloid.—Vegetal substance, basic and with strong physiological action.

Ament.—Raceme resembling a spike, usually made up of unisexual flowers and pendulum most of the time.

Amentiform.—Similar to Ament.

Angular, a.—Provided with angles.

Apetalous.—Without petals.

Axil.—Higher angle formed by a lateral organ (leaf, bract, etc.), joining the caulinar in which it is inserted.

Axillar.—Placed on the axil.

Beneath.—Opposite of above in leaves, etc.

Berry.—Pulpous fruit, indeshicent, containing many or few seeds and without a real stone, such as seen in grapes.

Bifid, a.—Said of the organ (leaf, foliole, etc.) divided into two segments that do not reach halfway of its total length.

Biotype.—Synonymous of biological form.

Bipinnate, a.—Twice pinnate.

Brachyblast.—Sprig with very short internodes, usually of limited growth with very close together leaves.

Bract.—Foliaceous organ, different from the leaf, associated with the flower or inflorescence.

Calyptra.—Kind of cap that protects the vegetative cone of the root. Also the structure formed as the result of the union of the petals and lobes of the calyx in the Eucalyptus flower.

Capitulum.—Inflorescences made up of sessil flowers on a very short, wide axis.

Capsule.—Dry fruit, dehiscent, formed by the union of two or more carpels.

Carpellary leaf.—Each one of the units that make up the pistil.

Cyathium.—Inflorescence typical formation. The female flower reduced to one pistil and the male flowers reduced to one stamen.

Cincinnus.—Scorpioid cyme in which the twigs it consists of grow to the right and left alternatively.

Cone.—Inflorescence consisting of a central axis on which naked, unisexual flowers and the tectrix bracts are inserted. The cones grow on coniferous species such as pines, firs, etc.

Cordate, a.—Synonymous of cordiform.

Cordiform.—Heart-shaped.

Corymb.—Racemose, simple inflorescence characterized by peduncles that start from different heights, although the flowers are at the same level.

Corymbiform.—Corymb-shaped.

Crenulate, a.—Festooned with small festoons.

Cultivate.—Cultivated variety. Group of cultivated plants easy to distinguish for their morphological and phisiological characteristics and that keep their characteristics when they reproduce sexually or asexually.

Cuneate, a.—Wedge-shaped.

Cyme.—Defined inflorescences whose axis end in a flower, as well as in the secondary lateral axes.

Deciduous, a.—With shedding leaves.

Dehiscent.—That opens.

Digitate, a.—Said of the leaves, bracts, etc., divided into deep diverging lobes that start from a point, like the fingers in an open hand.

Dioecious, a.—Plants with unisexual flowers: the male and female flowers being on different plants.

Drupe.—Fleshy fruit, monocarpellate, indehiscent, with a stone inside it.

Ellipsoidal.—Having an elliptical profile.

Endocarp.—Inner layer of the pericarp.

Endosperm.—Reserve tissue of seed.

Ensiform.—Sword-shaped.

Evergreen.—With perennial leaves.

Evergreen, a.—With perennial leaves.

Face.—Uper surface of the leaf.

Festooned, a.—Bordered with festoons.

Follicle.—Dry fruit, dehiscent, monocarpellate, that only opens along a single grooved line.

Foliole.—Foliaceous organ joined to the rachis of a leaf or its divisions.

Glabrous.—Hairless.

Glandular.—Provided with glands.

Glaucous.—Light green-bluish.

Gynoecium.—Group of the female organs of the flower.

Hermaphrodite.—Bisexual.

Imparipinnate, a.—Used to describe a pinnate leaf that terminates in a foliole.

Indehiscent.—That which does not open.

Inflorescence.—Group of flowers, arranged in a determined form, each plant wich its own characteristics.

Infrutescence.—Group of fruits proceeding from an inflorecence.

Infundibular.—Funnel-shaped.

Laciniate, a.—Divided into deep, narrow lobes.

Legume.—A dry, dehiscent, mono-carpellate fruit, which opens along the ventral suture and the middle nerve, characteristic of the leguminosae.

Blade.—Laminar parte of the leaf.

Linear.—Long and narrow, with parallel, or almost parallel edges.

Lobular, a.—Divided into lobules.

Macroblast.—Long shoots which form or prolong the branches.

Mericarp.—Each of the parts into which a schizocarp divides.

Mesocarp.—Middle layer of the pericarp.

Monoecious, a.—Used to describe plants with unisexual feminine and masculine flowers on the same plant.

Mucronate, a.—Ending in a short point.

Muricate, a.—With thorns or spines.

Oblanceolate, a.—Used to describe laminas (leaves, petals, etc.) in the form of a lance, but in reverse, that is, with the wider part at the top, and the narrower part at the base.

Obovate, a.—Egg-shaped, with the wider part at the top.

Obtuse, a.—Foliar organ (bract, leaf, etc.) the edges of which form an obtuse angle at the top.

Orbicular.—Circular.

Ovoid.—Egg-shaped.

Palmatilobate.—Used to describe a foliaceous organ wich palmate nervation, the bottom half of which is divided into very clear, almoast round lobules.

Panduriform.—Guitar-shaped.

Panicle.—A branching raceme.

Paniculate.—Arranges in panicles.

Paripinnate.—Used to describe a pinnate leaf wich an even number of folioles.

Peduncle.—Leaf-stalk of a flower or an inflorescence.

Pericarp.—The wall of the fruit. Usually made up of three layers, the external (epicarp), the internal (endocarp) and between them, the mesocarp.

Petiole.—Stalk that joins the blade of a leave with the stem.

Pinna.—Synonymous of foliole.

Pinnate, a.—With the parts (veins, folioles, etc.) arranged along both sides of an axis, similar to the barbs on the shaft of a feather.

Pinnately parted.—Foliaceous organ with pinnate veins in which the divisions of the segments reach the central vein.

Pistil.—Unit of the gynoecium consisting of ovary, style and stigma.

Pistillode.—Aborted pistil.

Polygamous, a.—Said of the plants with hermaphrodite and unisexual flowers on the same plant or on different ones.

Pubescent.—Covered with soft, short, fine hairs.

Pyriform.—Pear-shaped.

Raceme.—Inflorescence formed by an axis with pedunculate flowers on both sides.

Racemose.—Group of fruits originating from an inflorescence.

Rachis.—Axis of an inflorescence or of a compound leaf.

Reniform.—Kidney-shaped.

Revolute.—Said of the leaves whose edges are turned inside down.

Schizocarp.—Dry, dehiscent fruit that breaks up in mericarps.

Sepal.—Each one of the leaves of the calyx.

Serrated, a.—Synonymous of serrate.

Serrated, a.—Said of the foliaceous organs provided with sharp, clustered teeth along the edges, resembling a saw.

Sessile.—Without stem or base. A sessile leaf does not have a petiole.

Sinuous.—With sinuses.

Spadiciform.—Spadix-shaped.

Spadix.—Tassel with fleshy flowers, usually unisexual and surrounded by spathes.

Spathe.—Bract that wraps the spadix, sometimes large and reddish.

Stamen.—Flower organ having pollinic sacs with the pollen.

Strobila.—Synonymous for cone.

Syconus.—Fruit of the plants of the *Ficus genus.* It is racemose with a fleshy receptacle with tiny fruits.

Syncarp.—Group of joined fruits either belonging to one flower or to different flowers.

Tannin.—Vegetal, astringent substances used in tanning and for making dyes.

Tassel.—Racemose, simple inflorescence with sessile flowers.

Thornless.—Without prickles or spines.

Tomentum.—Group of interwined hairs resembling goat's hair.

Toothed, a.—Said of foliaceous organs such as leaves and petals with edges resembling a saw, but with less sharp teeth.

Triad.—Group of three.

Truncate, a.—With the apex cut off.

Umbel.—Racemose inflorescence with an axis from whose end grow pedicels of the same length.

Unisexual.—Having only one sex.

Verticillate, a.—Arranged in verticils.

Verticil.—Group of two or more organs (leaves, bracts, *etc.*) all growing at the same level.

Whose edges form an acute angle.

ALPHABETICAL INDEX
OF SCIENTIFIC NAMES

ALPHABETICAL INDEX
OF FAMILIES

ALPHABETICAL INDEX OF VULGAR NAMES

OF THE PLANTS

Coprosma repens	MIRROR PLANT
Cordyline australis	GIANT DRACAENA
Corynocarpus laevigata	NEW ZEALAND LAUREL
Crescentia cujete	CALABASH TREE
Cycas revoluta	SAGO PALM
Delonix regia	FLAMBOYANT
Erythrina crista-galli	COCKSPUR CORAL TREE
Eucalyptus ficifolia	RED-FLOWERING GUM
Eugenia uniflora	SURINAM CHERRY
Euphorbia pulcherrima	POINSETTIA
Feijoa sellowiana	FEIJOA
Ficus aspera	CLOWN FIG
Ficus benjamina	BENJAMIN TREE
Ficus elastica	INDIA RUBBER TREE
Ficus lyrata	FIDDLE-LEAF FIG
Ficus macrophylla	MORETONBAY FIG
Ficus microcarpa	LAUREL FIG
Ficus rubiginosa	RUSTY FIG
Ficus sycomorus	SYCAMORE FIG
Ginkgo biloba	MAIDENHAIR TREE
Grevillea robusta	SILKY OAK
Greyia radlkoferi	TRANSVAAL BOTTLEBRUSH
Hibiscus rosa-sinensis	CHINESE HIBISCUS, ROSE-OF-CHINA
Hibiscus schizopetalus	JAPANESE HIBISCUS
Howea belmoreana	BELMOR SENTRY PALM
Howea forsteriana	KENTIA, SENTRY PALM
Jacaranda mimosifolia	JACARANDA
Jubaea chilensis	CHILEAN WINE PALM
Kigelia africana	SAUSAGE TREE
Lagunaria patersonii	NORFOLK ISLAND HIBISCUS
Lantana camara	YELLOW SAGE
Livistona chinensis var. chinensis	CHINESE FAN PALM
Macadamia integrifolia	MACADAMIA NUT
Mackaya bella	MACKAYA
Mammea americana	MAMEY

Mangifera indica	MANGO
Megaskepasma erythrochlamys	BRAZILIAN RED-CLOAK
Microcoelum weddelianum	WEDDEL PALM
Nandina domestica	HEAVENLY BAMBOO
Nerium oleander	COMMON OLEANDER
Nuxia floribunda	WHITE ELDER
Ochna serrulata	MICKEY-MOUSE PLANT
Pandanus utilis	COMMON SCREW PINE
Parkinsonia aculeata	JERUSALEM THORN
Persea americana	AVOCADO
Phoenix dactylifera	DATE PALM
Phoenix reclinata	SENEGAL DATE PALM
Phoenix roebelinii	PYGMY DATE PALM
Phytolacca dioica	OMBÚ
Psidium guajava	COMMON GUAVA
Rhapis excelsa	BAMBOO PALM
Roystonea regia	CUBAN ROYAL PALM
Schinus molle	PEPPER TREE
Schinus terebinthifolius	BRAZILIAN PEPPER TREE
Sparmannia africana	AFRICAN HEMP
Spathodea campanulata	TULIP TREE
Syzygium jambos	ROSE APPLE
Tecoma stans	YELLOW ELDER
Terminalia catappa	TROPICAL ALMOND
Tipuana tipu	ROSEWOOD
Trachycarpus fortunei	WINDMILL PALM
Washingtonia filifera	DESERT FAN PALM
Washingtonia robusta	THREAD PALM
Yucca aloifolia	SPANISH-BAYONET

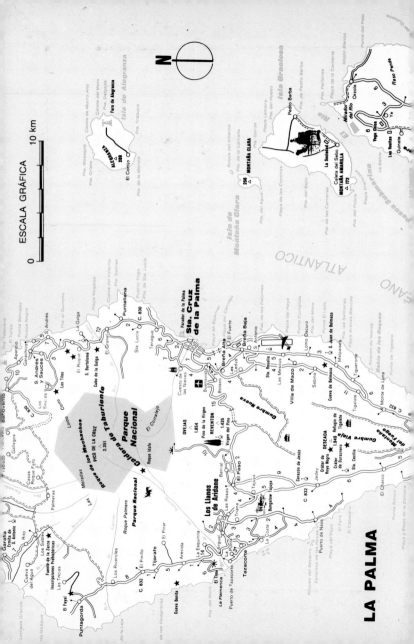

LA PALMA

ESCALA GRÁFICA

10 km

OCÉANO ATLÁNTICO